National Museum

Publishers: George A. Christopoulos, John C. Bastias
Translation: David Hardy
Managing Editor: Efi Karpodini
Art Director: Chrysé Daskalopoulou
Special Photography: Spyros Tsavdaroglou, Makis Skiadaresis and Nikos Kontos
Colour separation: Pietro Carlotti
Fototypesetting: Compu-Libro — Athanasiou

Printed and bound in Greece by

Ekdotike Hellados S.A., Athen

National Museum

ILLUSTRATED GUIDE TO THE MUSEUM

Dr. SEMNI KAROUZOU

Honorary Ephor of the National Museum of Athens

EKDOTIKE ATHENON S.A.
Athens 1996

ISBN 960-213-004-0

Copyright © 1977
Ekdotike Athenon S.A.
1, Vissarionos St., Athens 106 72
Printed in Greece

THE HISTORY OF THE NATIONAL MUSEUM

The Greek Museums would contain only fragments of ancient marbles and other works, were it not for the fact that the Greek soil never tires of yielding up its gifts. Divine figures, carved by important artists, are continually coming to the light of day, vases are continually being discovered buried in tombs, and splendid bronze statuettes are revealed from time to time by the discovery of an ancient shrine or sanctuary.

The organised plundering of ancient works would be the main reason so many of them are now lost. It began in the second century B.C., with the relentless sacking of the ancient cities on the orders of the Roman generals, and it has never stopped throughout the following centuries, though now it is less systematic. The mania has revived in modern times, though from different motives.

European lovers of antiquity, collectors and merchants, some of them moved by the spirit of the Renaissance and the esteem in which it held the ancient world, others driven by a passion for profit, hastened to the enslaved

Greek sites, either to study there (especially from the eighteenth century onwards) or to pillage. We may concede to the best of this latter group the mitigating factor that they were enchanted by Greek works of art and, particularly in the case of the English, wanted to adorn their palaces and country houses with them.

Long before the pure souls of the philhellenes spurred them on to come to the Classical lands and sacrifice themselves in the cause of Greek freedom, many of their fellow countrymen had destroyed the ancient sites throughout the Greek world and Asia Minor, and had taken with them everything of beauty and value they found standing, or that was handed over to them by the unsuspecting villagers.

The unique sight one meets inside the National Museum, indeed its whole character, is closely connected with the appearance of the first archaeological societies in Greece and with the very history of the Greek state, which commences with the declaration of independence in 1821. The National Museum differs from the museums of Europe in its direct connection with the Greek soil. The latter were created, as we saw, in the period before the Renaissance, and had as their basis private collections that consisted of a wide variety of finds, most of them coming from countries throughout the Roman Empire. In contrast, the objects that adorn the National Museum were all discovered in the Greek world, and most of them came from ancient temples and tombs; they were not used to decorate palaces, villas and Roman baths, and therefore have a certain sanctity, possessing an inspired creativity and spiritual depth.

At an early point in time the enslaved Greeks became conscious of the fact that though they were separated from the ancients by many centuries, they were nonetheless descended from them. And though the name "Hellenes" had been forgotten, and they were referred to as Christians or *Romaioi*, it began to come into general use from 1810. About 1800, Korais speaks of *Graeci,* but during the struggle for independence from Turkish rule and the years immediately following the name "Hellenes" was that predominantly used amongst the freedom fighters.

At the same time, a number of lettered Athenian aristocrats founded the "Society of Lovers of the Arts" in Athens, with the full support of the people; it had two main aims: "firstly the education of the youth, and secondly the preservation of the ruined and plundered glorious monuments of antiquity". The Englishman Lord Guildford was named honorary president in 1814.

When the enlightened patriot Kapodistrias came to take over the government of Greece, therefore, he found souls ready to welcome his creative plans. In 1829, the first Museum was constructed in the temporary capital, Aegina, and Kapodistrias appointed as Ephor Andreas Moustoxidis, a cultured Corfiote. The contents of the Museum, which consisted largely of private gifts, and were casual finds, were housed in the Home for Orphans, which was itself founded by Kapodistrias for the orphans of the combatants. The name "National Museum" is already used in the bill put before the government by Moustoxidis in December 1829, providing for the collecting and preserving of antiquities.

A short time later, in Athens, which was finally decided upon as the capital, the Ephor Kyriakos Pittakis, an enthusiastic patriot, began to collect together ancient sculptures in a number of different buildings. In 1836, when the Theseion was full, ancient objects were transferred to the "Stoa" of Hadrian, including many important pieces from the Museum on Aegina. The Theseion had been designated the future "Central Archaeological Museum", and to this end the Holy Synod gave the order in 1835 for the Holy Altar, and "every other thing found there connected with the church" to be removed from it.

In 1865, the government handed over rooms in the Varvakeion to house the collections assembled by the Archaeological Society in its own Museum since 1858. The building of a large Museum was made imperative, however, by the fact that the antiquities were scattered amongst several different buildings, and that their number was constantly growing, not only as a result of excavations, but also because they were being discovered beneath the humble dwellings that were being built in the small capital. The famous architect Leo von Klenze, who was the inspiration behind Neoclassical Munich, had, since 1835, had sufficiently official and serious plans ready for the National Museum, which he had called the "Pantechneion". Its construction was not begun until 1866, however, when Helen Tositsa presented a large plot of land for the purpose, and when a liberal donation had been made by Dimitrios Vernardakis, a Cretan from Saint Petersburg. The Greek state also provided assistance, and the west wing of the "Central Museum" was ready in 1881, and was immediately filled with antiquities. Next, in 1881, a royal order of 19th April, procured on the initiative of Charilaos Trikoupis, determined that its name should be changed to the "National Archaeological Museum".

Not long afterwards, in 1891, the Archaeological Society handed over to it the antiquities that its members had collected together out of devotion to their country. The building proceeded according to the plan of the distinguished architect Ernst Ziller, based, with some changes, on an older plan which is unfortunately now lost, but which had been produced by Lange, an architect of the Romantic School and pupil of the painter Rotman.

From the very beginning, the contents of the scattered archaeological collections, belonging to the Archaeological Society and ultimately to the National Museum, inspired both Greek and foreign archaeologists in their academic research work. The works of ancient art grew constantly in number as a result of the excavations of the former, and also of the foreign archaeological schools.

From as early as the second decade of the twentieth century, the rooms in the Museum were overcrowded, and the antiquities jumbled together, with no attempt at aesthetic display. The only direction in which it was possible to extend it was towards the east. The financial means to commence the building of this extension were furnished in 1931 by the then Minister of Education, George Papandreou.

In 1939, when the new wing was ready, the offices were first to be transferred there. In 1940, however, the outbreak of the war between Italy and

Greece not only prevented the transfer of some of the antiquities there, but also made it necessary to remove every item from the old building in order to bury them.

It was not until after the civil war, in 1945, that money was first supplied by Alexandros Mylonas, the Minister for Economic Affairs, for the unpacking of the antiquities. Times were difficult and there was little credit available, so that Christos Karouzos, who had been Director of the National Museum since 1942, had to encourage the technical staff to assist in removing the sand from the cellars without pay, which they willingly agreed to do, beginning with the cellars in which the sculptures were stored.

It was the beginning of the rebirth of the Museum. The old building of Lange and Ziller stood in need of general repair, and to some extent of adaptation, for the ancient works of art had until then stood insecurely on the floor formed by a deep layer of earth.

While the exhibition of the pottery was being prepared, the basic repairs to the old building continued, with American assistance through the Marshall Aid scheme, and a gift from the Greek state. Since the restoration of the old building was clearly a long-term undertaking, however, it was decided to mount a temporary exhibition of the most representative items in the Museum in the ten rooms on the ground floor of the new wing. This made it possible for the young people who had grown up not knowing the antiquities to become familiar with ancient art, and for the people to derive pleasure from them, as well as the travellers, who at that time were few, but were insistent, and many of whom had a Classical education.

When the work on the old building was completed, the exhibition of vases and pottery on the upper floor of the new wing was well advanced. The Mycenaean room and the two smaller adjoining rooms were the first to be officially inaugurated, and thanks to the intensive efforts of the staff, both academic and technical, the sculpture rooms were opened to the public one after the other; the Archaic sculpture rooms presented a splendidly bright appearance, and there were five large and two smaller rooms to replace the single hall that had housed both Archaic and Archaising sculpture in the pre-War exhibition.

While the work of displaying the sculptures in the rooms of the old building continued, intensive work in the laboratories made it possible to clean and display the glorious bronzes from Dodona, and to open the Karapanos Room, named after the patriot from Epirus who had donated them to the Greek state.

After Helen Stathatos had generously presented her valuable collection of gold and other works of art, a special room was set aside for them to the right of the main entrance to the Museum, and named "The Gift of Helen and Konst. Stathatos".

The plan to organise the final exhibition of the unique collection of bronzes in the Museum was only effectively realised in 1964. Two rooms housed the marvellous bronzes from Olympia, the Acropolis and other Greek sites (more detailed description of these rooms).

This guide to the National Museum is subject to change, pending completion of the new exhibition of its archaeological treasures.

VISITING THE NATIONAL MUSEUM

The visitor begins with the three prehistoric rooms. The two narrow side rooms are described before the large Mycenaean room in the centre. The one on the left houses finds from the Neolithic period, along with a number of more recent ones, and the corresponding room on the right contains marble Cycladic figurines, vases, and other discoveries from the Bronze Age.

The first room on the left of the main entrance forms an introduction to the sculpture rooms, both large and small; before the last of them is reached there is an opening onto the interior courtyard, an open area with statues and reliefs in its porticoes. After the second large room containing funerary reliefs, one may pass through to the room of the Diadoumenos and the room of the "open air" altar. Before proceeding to the other sculpture rooms, the visitor will find it easiest to visit the Karapanos room, and then part of a room containing statuettes and vessels of bronze. The second floor is occupied by eight rooms of clay objects, vases, figurines, and a number of bronzes, dating from the Geometric period to the end of the fourth century B.C.; the three rooms of the Numismatic Museum and the room with finds from the excavations on Thera.

Returning to the central room of the altar, the visitor may proceed to the rest of the large sculpture rooms with material from ancient shrines and tombs. On the west and north sides of them are smaller rooms overlooking the courtyard of the Epigraphic Museum, which contain small votive reliefs from the Asklepieia of Athens and Piraeus, the Amphiareion at Oropos, and other sanctuaries.

GROUND PLAN OF THE MAIN FLOOR OF
THE NATIONAL ARCHAEOLOGICAL MUSEUM

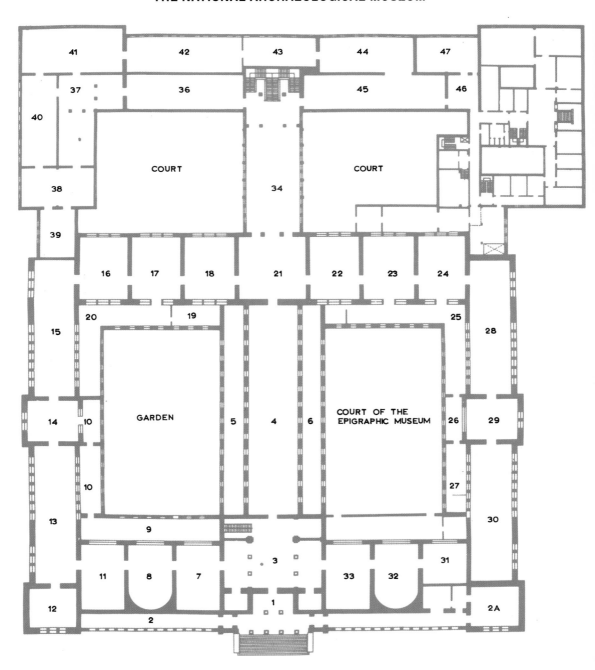

PLAN OF THE 1ST FLOOR OF THE NATIONAL ARCHAEOLOGICAL MUSEUM

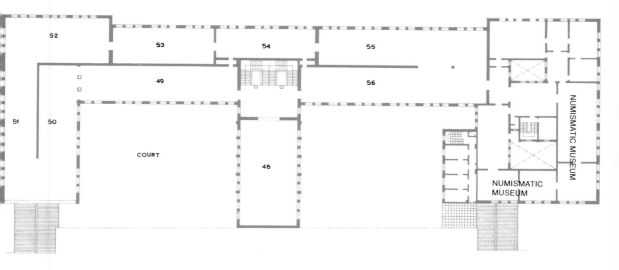

Plan of the main floor of the National Archaeological Museum

1. Porch 2. Northern stoa 2A. Exhibition of casts 3. Entrance Hall 4. Mycenaean room 5. Neolithic and Pre-Mycenaean room 6. Cycladic room 7. 1st room of Archaic sculpture 8. 2nd room of Archaic sculpture 9-10A. Small rooms of Archaic works 11. 3rd room of Archaic sculpture 12. 4th room of Archaic sculpture 13. Room of Aristodikos 14. Room containing Early Classical *stelai* (Gravestones) 15. Room of Poseidon 16. 1st room of Classical grave *stelai* 17. Room of Classical votive reliefs 18. 2nd room of Classical grave *stelai* 19-20. Two small rooms of Classical works 21. Room of the Diadoumenos 22. Room of Epidauros 23. 1st room of grave *stelai* of the 4th century B.C. 24. 2nd room of grave monuments of the 4th century B.C. 25. Two rooms of decree and votive reliefs 26. 3rd small room of votive reliefs 27. 4th small room of votive reliefs 28. Grave monuments of the 4th century B.C. Room of the Youth from Antikythera 29. Room of Themis 30. Room of Hellenistic sculpture 31, 32, 33. Rooms of sculpture (under rearrangement, temporarily closed) 34. Room of the altar 35. Staircase to the 1st floor 36. Karapanos Collection (bronzes) 37-39. Rooms of bronzes (under rearrangement, temporarily closed, except part of 37) 40. Stathatos Collection and gold objects (under rearrangement, temporarily closed) 41. Collection of clay figurines (under rearrangement, temporarily closed) 42-45. Rooms for temporary exhibitions.

Plan of the 1st floor

48. The Thera frescoes 49. Room of Geometric vases 50. Room of Geometric vases from different workshops 51. Room of Vari vases 52. Room of Heraeum of Argos and Sophilos 53. Room of black-figure vases 54. Room of black-figure and red-figure vases 55. Room of white-ground lekythoi — red-figure vases — Choe 56. Room of vases of the 4th century B.C. Room of epinetron of Eretria.

GROUND PLAN OF THE MAIN FLOOR OF
THE NATIONAL ARCHAEOLOGICAL MUSEUM

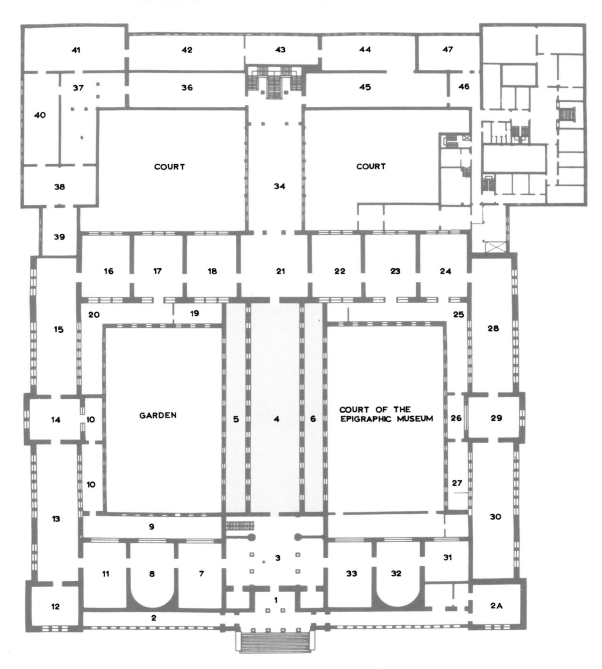

Prehistoric Collections. 4: Mycenaean room 5: Neolithic and Premycenaean room 6: Cycladic room

Prehistoric Collections

PRE-MYCENAEAN ROOM

The first of the rooms housing the prehistoric collection, to the left of the large Mycenaean room, was created during the post-War years to relieve the overcrowded condition of the objects from the Neolithic period and the Bronze Age objects from the Cyclades.

It is to Christos Tsountas that we owe the discovery of the Neolithic civilisation of Thessaly. In his travels in the Thessalian plain – which must have been very difficult at that time – he noted the existence of a large number of *magoulas* (mounds), and, selecting a region not far to the west of Volos, he made systematic excavations of the sites of Sesklo and Dimini and uncovered acropoleis, dwellings and a vast number of objects from the Neolithic period.

When, about 2000 B.C., the first Greek tribes came down to Thessaly from the North, they did not find the area totally devoid of human existence. Thousands of years earlier a civilisation had developed and the arts had been practised. The latest researches of M. Milojčic and D. Theocharis at other Thessalian centres have established the existence of pre-ceramic levels and shown clearly that the use of clay to make pots was developed gradually immediately after these levels by the same people, and was not the result of an incursion of foreign peoples.

The first Greek tribes to come down in groups from the North found a developed civilisation, and fused with it in what appears to

No. 5894 Clay figurine of a seated male

have been a peaceful manner. New worlds and new forms were born from this union, perhaps the most important of which was the religion. This marked an important stage in the history of Europe, and was the moment when "the Greek people was its historic bearer. The Greek vision about the world formed the world to come, and the Greek deity appears; here is the Greek myth". (Paola Philippson).

As a result of recent research, the chronology, which is of course relative rather than absolute, has been put back further than that suggested by Tsountas, though it is still based on his view that the culture of Sesklo is older than that of Dimini. The chronology of the different phases as suggested by the two scholars referred to above is as follows, though further research may be expected to lower the dates somewhat:

7th millennium: Pre-ceramic period
6th millennium: Early Neolithic period
5th millennium: Middle Neolithic period
4th millennium: Late Neolithic period.

It has become established practice to apply the term "Sesklo period" to Early Neolithic finds from other sites as well.

Case 34: Finds from Sesklo

In the first small showcase on the wall, the monochrome "Proto-Sesklo style" vases without handles have simple shapes. No. **6034**, however, has a low base and calyx-shaped rim. The desire to give a certain liveliness to them led to the invention of the slip, which is sometimes a reddish colour (nos. **6025** and **6028**).

On a separate stand: Statuette of a seated male

The large clay figurine of a seated male, no. **5894**, from Thessaly, more probably dates from the end of the Neolithic period than the beginning of the Bronze Age. The emphasis on the male member suggests that it represented a fertility god.

Cases 35-36: Finds from the acropolis of Sesklo

In the larger case 35, no. **5925**, a handleless bowl with open rim and a series of broken lines on the white slip, presents a virgin picture. Even modern craftsmen are envious of the simple broad decoration on this large fragment.

The wealth of stone tools – axes, chisels, and blades of flint and obsidian – and of others made of bone, affords evidence for the struggles of the people of those times to survive by hunting, farming, the construction of settlements, and also by spinning and weaving (spindlewhorls).

The clay figurines are steatopygous and simply shaped, stongly suggesting fertility, and normally depict female standing figures; they must be representations of the Great Goddess, the primeval Mother Goddess of the Aegean. The larger seated figure of the *kourotrophos* (nursing mother), no. **5937**, (case 36) with her baby in her arms, is later than the end of the Neolithic period. The white stone figurine from Sesklo, no. **5936**, (in a small wall-case, along with schematic stone figurines from Sesklo of the Late Neolithic period) has been enlivened by the addition of red decoration. The deep *phiale*, no. **5932** (case 35) with large spiral and meander decoration, is transitional from *Sesklo Style* to *Dimini Style*. The fragments of a vase (fruit-stand), no. **5921** (case 35), with white decoration on a reddish surface, are from the acropolis of Sesklo.

No. 5937 Clay figurine of a Kourotrophos

Case 49: Finds from Dimini

"Dimini Style" is a general term derived from the finds on the acropolis at Dimini, which is better fortified and had a megaron in the centre of the courtyard.

The cup no. **5920**, without a base, is divided into areas decorated with the chessboard pattern and primitive meanders in dull colours. The decoration of the inner surface of the vase no. **5922** (on a separate base) shows an architectonic sense astonishing in such an early period. Unprecedented grasp and imagination are shown in its graceful spherical shape, and in the decoration around it, which takes the form of patterns of confidently drawn black curvilinear bands; the red patterns interwoven with them enliven the picture. Foreign influences from the North spring to mind as an explanation of these unprecedented motifs in the Dimini style, since colonisation by newcomers is highly unlikely.

Case 37: Finds from Dimini

The small figurines are now local and unskillful, and have lost the primitive richness and god-like appearance found in the earlier ones from the acropolis of Sesklo. The shapes and decoration of the pots, however, are revolutionary particularly in the painted motifs.

Case 40: Finds from Boeotia, Phthiotis

The famous spherical vase no. **8051** was found further south at Lianokladi, Lamia; it is related, though not closely, to that from Dimini. The thin lines round the body are like wires, and the question arises as to the influences which are behind a shape like this, at once complicated and unaffected.

Case 47: Finds from Halai, Lokris

The simple pure shapes of the Neolithic cups from Halai, Lokris, still have a direct attraction for the modern visitor, uncluttered as they are by handles, base or any decoration.

Case 48: Finds from tholos tombs of Thessaly

The gold ornaments from graves at Volos and Dimini, chief amongst them a five-leafed Minoan lily (no. **5607**), form a Mycenaean interlude.

Case 41: Finds from Lemnos

The finds from Poliochni, on Lemnos (four periods from 2700-2200 B.C.) are more significant than all the rest because their connections are with objects not from the islands but from Troy (see case 44).

Case 42: Finds from Attica

Finds from dwellings and tombs on the promontory of Aghios Kosmas. The monochrome vases are lifeless (second half of the third millennium). Evidence for communication is afforded by the Cycladic "frying pans" (nos. **8956**, **8959**), with incised decoration, and also by the small, very schematic, Cycladic marble figurines (nos. **8970-8976**) and some pieces of obsidian (no. **8996**). Though the vases could be taken as evidence of the trading activities of Cycladic seafarers, they were in fact produced locally.

No. 5922 Spherical vase from Dimini

No. 8051 Spherical vase from Lianokladi, Lamia

No. 7159 Gold jewellery from Poliochni on Lemnos

On separate stands: Vases

Nos. **5875-6**. Middle Helladic *pithoi* with typical large-scale linear decoration. First half of the second millennium. No. **5877**. The largest and most striking Early Helladic vase is exhibited in the middle of the wall (from Orchomenos). It has no base, but has a tall body which swells out as it rises, and a calyx-shaped mouth. As one looks at it, one is overwhelmed by the formal unity of the apparently simple but in fact studiedly sober shape. From the Early Helladic II period, 2200-2000 B.C.

THE CYCLADIC ROOM

The section in the National Museum that houses the Cycladic objects consists of the pre-War room, where all the finds of the prehistoric period (Neolithic as well as Bronze Age) had been stored, together with the neighbouring room, which held the Egyptian antiquities and which was formerly an offshoot of the Mycenaean room.

Cycladic Civilisation

Although the islands are separated from each other — the ancients called them the Cyclades, because they believed they centred round the small island of Delos, sacred to Apollo — they developed during the Bronze Age, as early as the end of the third millennium, a culture that was uniform and peculiar to itself, with no connections with the Helladic or any other culture. The earliest inhabitants of the Aegean — called Carians by Thucydides — did not live only by cultivating crops and rearing animals on their rocky islands. Skilled sailors succeeded in selling the chief product of the islands, the obsidian of Melos, as far as Attica. The sea surrounding the islands was the chief source of their prosperity, and in turn explains their charming art.

The marble figurines dominate the Cycladic room. All, with few exceptions, are female, and today they enchant student and visitor alike. For many decades they have been the sources of inspiration for European artists. The island astists created the white figures of the naked female deity, the "Mother Goddess" of the Aegean, inspired by the marble of Paros, in particular, and also that of Naxos. Their activity recalls the skilled work of the sculptors who lived many centuries later on Naxos, and especially Paros. In the Classical period the warm, creative marble of this island was called *lychnites* because lamps (*lychnoi*) were used when the guarrymen went down into the dark quarries.

Scattered finds drew the attention of archaeologists in the last century to the existence of a Cycladic culture, but it is to Christos Tsountas first and foremost that we owe the systematic excavation and scholarly publication of the discoveries that demonstrated beyond doubt the existence of a uniform Cycladic culture in the Bronze Age. He found over 450 graves on Syros alone, others on Paros, Antiparos, Siphnos and even Despotiko.

On separate stands

No. **3978**. The largest and best preserved of the Cycladic figurines was discovered on Amorgos. Its legs are unusually long and are only slightly separated, the feet point downward, while the loins are separated plastically with the female parts outlined. The arms are folded (the left always above the right) over the abdomen, which is almost

No. 3978 Large Cycladic marble figurine from Amorgos

flat. They are inexcusably thin for such a work. The breasts too are set very high. However, the upright neck and the long head with its straight skull above the high forehead form a noble crown for the work. Today the only indication of facial expression is the nose, but originally the eyes and mouth will have been shown in lightly painted colours. Its whole presence, silent and distant, hides some secret meaning.

No. **3909**. The large head from Amorgos is more impressive and more important as a work of art. In comparison with the preceding figurine it is more rounded, and even the forehead has become curved, like the jaw, which juts out to a point above the narrow neck, shaped almost like a column. As if in reaction to the schematic flatness of it, the sculptor has raised the lips plastically, and the mouth is open. Few heads rendered naturalistically give so good an expression of introspection, of a people, of a period. This head is dated, like so many marble figurines, to the Middle Cycladic period.

The periods of the Cycladic culture have the following names, derived from the names of sites in the islands: the first phase (2800-2400) is called Pelos-Lakkoudes, the middle (2400-2200) Keros-Syros, and the third (2200-2000) Phylakopi I, from the city of Phylakopi on Melos.

A number of steatopygous and fiddle-shaped figurines from the Cyclades are thought to be survivals from the Neolithic period, although the most recent of them seem to continue for a long time. It is astonishing how the Cycladic figurines have a distinct personality, even though they fall within the general type of the naked goddess: no two are exactly alike, even though some may have been carved in the same workshop.

Case 59: Finds from Syros

A number of figurines from Syros are suddenly distinguished by the angular spreading of the shoulders, standing well apart from the chest. The arms are open (no. **6174**). The head no longer has the shape of an ellipse, but is closer to that of a triangle, and it is no longer tilted – a feature well known in other figurines. The new phenomenon of the raising of the abdomen has been interpreted as suggesting pregnancy. The delicate hand of another Cycladic artist can be seen in the small fine *kylix* no. **5021**. Similar ones have been found on the other islands too.

Case 72: Finds from Amorgos

The figurine from Amorgos, no. **4719**, is more advanced. The elevation of the buttocks is unusual, the legs are graceful, and an early sense of Greekness can be dimly discerned in this statue. Only a few of the Cycladic figurines were found in settlements, most of them coming from graves, where they had been placed next to the dead.

On separate stands: Figurines of musicians

Two of the very rare male Cycladic figurines, the very beautiful and much praised figures of the *first musicians of the Greek world,* were found in 1884 on Keros, a deserted island opposite Amorgos used only as a grazing ground. In the first of them (no. **3910**) a naked male figure is holding two pipes to his mouth with his hands; the second depicts a seated man playing the harp (no. **3908**). He will have been some official bard or hero, for he is sitting on a rich throne.

No. 6174 Cycladic marble female figurine

His ecstasy is conveyed by the head being distinctly tilted up and back above the strong neck. He has been called Orpheus – an attempt to find some mythical name for this dreamlike figure. The astonishing achievement of the sculptor is marked not only by the perfect carving, but also by the way the figure is rendered in all dimensions and dominates the space. It is superior to the other two figurines of harpists (no. **8833**, case 53), which are seated on a stool rather than a throne. What purpose can these musicians have served in the graves, other than to charm the dead man and to comfort him in the other world with the sound of music?

Cases 56-57: Cycladic vases

In contrast with Crete and Greece, where the potter's wheel was known from roughly 2000 B.C., the Cycladic pots of the first and middle phases of the Bronze Age remain handmade. A curious type of pot, the frying-pan shaped (cases 56-57), is best known from the cemeteries of Chalandriani on Syros, where Tsountas excavated with such rich results. On one side, the outer surface, they are decorated with incised motifs of triangles, or more frequently spirals. They were emphasised by colours prepared in the mortars discovered in the excavations. Many theories have been propounded about the function of these pots, but the old view of Tsountas remains unshaken. Observing that their undecorated hollow inner surfaces were smooth and polished, he conjectured that they were filled with water and used as mirrors, especially by women. The pubic triangle incised low down on them is most probably connected with this use (no. **4974**, case 57). A high-prowed ship is incised on two of these vessels, with a fish suspended above the figure-head (no. **5230**, case 57). Two rows of oars are indicated by fine lines along the length of the boat. The spiraliform decoration around the ships must surely in this instance represent the waves of the foaming sea, the waves of the Aegean.

Cases 52, 53, 54, 55, 61, 73: Finds from Naxos and Syros

Important discoveries in the form of figurines, vessels of both marble and clay, tools, and other items have been yielded by recent excavations of cemeteries at a number of sites on Naxos.

Some of the marble figurines discovered (nos. **6195** and **6140.22**, case 73, no. **6140.21**, case 52) are amongst the finest products of Cycladic sculpture. The head stands above the tall neck, tilted slightly back, and the shoulders are thrust forward. In all the figurines of this type, there is generally a groove between the legs, but the loins do not always project, as in the powerful no. **6195**, case 53. No. **6140. 21**, case 53, is flat, long and narrow, and some of the smaller ones are completely schematic and shapeless, with only an impression of the arms being given, no indication of the breasts, and the slender neck made too long. The schematisation is carried to extremes in some of the figurines, which scarcely suggest the human form at all (nos. **6140.3**, and **8830**, case 52). The inventive sculptors were not satisfied with only a few types. In the figurine no. **6140.16**, case 53, as though in reaction against the elongated shape, the neck is shorter, the shoulders extended, and the arms and legs are rendered in plastic elevation, as if in an attempt to depict the female form more naturalistically.

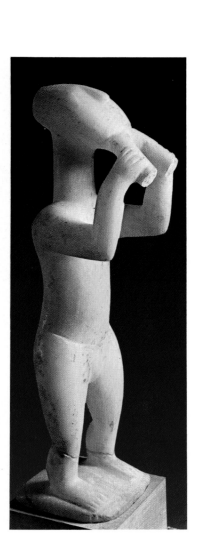

No. 3910 Marble figurine of a flute-player

No. 3908 Magnificent Cycladic figurine of a harpist. From Keros

3908

No. 6184 Clay utensil in the shape of a "frying pan"

No. 6176 Vase in the shape of a bear

No. 5782 Base of a vase with a scene of fishermen

The heavy marble collared jars ("oil-lamps") with pierced handles, nos. **6110**, **6133.3**, case 55, are great achievements. The fine Cycladic sensibility is clearer on the small vase no. **6133.2**, case 52, and on the stone *pyxis* no. **6133.5**, case 52.

Of the clay vases from the cemeteries on Naxos the typical Cycladic *pyxides* are dark grey in colour with fine incisions: zig-zag lines, herring-bone pattern in horizontal (no. **6101**, case 55) or vertical arrangement.

One of the best examples of the painted decoration is the vase with the three lamps, no. **6108**, case 53. This was also dedicated in a grave after it had been used in life, and it shows the quality of the everyday pottery; so does the charming beaked cup no. **6107**, case 73, from the same grave in the cemetery of Spedos; the marble figurine no. **6195**, case 73, was also found here, along with a number of other beautiful pots with linear decoration.

The plastic vase in the shape of a bear or other animal, from Syros, no. **6176**, case 61, with dark designs on a light surface, is quite unexpected amongst this pottery. It is holding a deep bowl in its hands which opens towards the animal's neck, suggesting a magical use. The headless figurine of a harpist, no. **8833**, case 53, from the cemetery of Aphentika on Naxos, would not be worthy of comparison with the splendid example from Keros, no. **3908**, case 52, even if it were in a better state of preservation. He is sitting on a stool, not a throne like the other harpist.

Cases 72 and 58: Finds from Amorgos and Syros

Our picture of the Cycladic graves would be one-sided if we did not devote some attention to the small number of ornaments and the large number of tools. A pin was found on the shoulder of a skeleton in a tomb at Chalandriani, no. **5120**, case 58, and a simple silver diadem in a tomb on Amorgos, no. **4729**, case 72. Other discoveries are: bracelets, bone beads of a variety of shapes, chisels, and also bronze lances, tools, a great number of metal tweezers and pins of both bronze and bone; and naturally obsidian blades and needles.

What is impressive in this room, amongst other things, is the autonomy of the Cycladic culture. During the period when the whole of Greece was obsessed with the fever of bronze, they produced an original art as a result of their geographical position, their racial composition and other factors beyond our grasp. We sense above all in this room a gentle tender art, the devotion of the people of the Cyclades to the divine, and a fine sensibility which, like so many other things, can still be found today amongst the inhabitants of the islands.

Cases 62-66: Finds from Melos

The antiquities from *Phylakopi* on Melos, a city which, though at the mercy of the north winds, also received its blessings, are collected together in the centre of the room. They were discovered during the excavations of the British School in 1903 and later.

The change in the shapes of the pots, and their decoration and motifs, compared with those well known from the Cyclades, makes an immediate impression. A later period of the Bronze Age finds its expression in these objects, the main new element being, above all, the introduction of nature: flowers and plants, flying birds (nos. **5762**, **5768**, case 66), reeds waving in the wind (nos. **5764**, **5735**, case 65) and "poppies" on an *oinochoe* (no. **5749**, case 66), the shape most commonly found in the second city of Phylakopi. Chronologically, we are now at the period about 1600 B.C., but the most important point is that the bearers of this culture were not Cycladic, but Cretan. Cretan motifs support the view that at this date Phylakopi had been captured and was inhabited by Cretans, who use it as a trading post (*emporion*). The *pithos* (no. **5841**), however, and the large bath (no. **5839**) with the fine curvilinear decoration (outside the cases), must be local works. The base of a vase with the unique picture of fishermen is also local work (no. **5782**, on a separate base). Dressed in short kilts, they are standing with their slender legs apart, holding a fish in each hand; the hands are shapeless. The bodies are drawn in outline and have been painted in a brown colour. What is particularly astonishing is the large round eye in the middle of the cheek, reminiscent of a Cyclop. The vase-painter must have been influenced by wall-paintings, since he succeeded in portraying the theme with clarity, especially the broad chest.

On the wall, at the back of the room: Frescoes

The portable plaque with the flying fish on a white surface (no. **5844**) of lime plaster was formerly regarded as the work of a Cretan painter, probably imported from Crete. The outlines are dark, but the dominating colour is the blue used for the wings and a large part of the body. The lavish depiction of the sea on this plaque is reminiscent of the frescoes of Thera, and perhaps indicative of the extent to which the Cycladic peoples attained the level of their Cretan teachers. The lily, a purely Cretan motif, which the Cretan colonists will have used to decorate the walls of their houses, appears in the surviving fragments of another fresco from Phylakopi (no. **5843**). White, on a dark background, it appears in the Phylakopi fresco to remind us of its origin.

No. 5844 Fresco with flying-fishes

THE MYCENAEAN ROOM

Mycenaean Art

"I look in astonishment" (θάμβος μ' έχει εσορόωντα). Astonishing indeed is the first sight of the large central room in the Museum housing the treasures of the Mycenaean period. What a surprise are the solid gold funeral masks of the kings, the gold cups, the engraved rings, the seal-stones, the bronze swords and knives, the ornaments made of all kinds of material, the remains of frescoes, the polychrome daggers, the large bronze *lebetes*, and the stone grave *stelai*. The display is almost a panorama of all the arts practised by the Mycenaeans and the other Greeks who shared in the Mycenaean culture. The rich exhibition of objects in this room is striking; the room is strange and macabre in places, but possesses a multicoloured and varied liveliness, even though most of the exhibits come from tombs. The whole array marks an interlude in the frugal, though often monumental, form of the objects in the Museum, and provokes a number of questions − above all, how, at that distant period, did so much gold come to be found so suddenly in Greece, the sterile, rocky country with which Poverty always walked hand in hand, as Herodotos emphasises. How did these richly adorned kings appear? Where were so many artists trained to practise their various crafts? Because of these difficulties, the

No. 2489 Silver cup with inlaid gold
male heads

No. 2468 Ivory head of a warrior

Mycenaean period is regarded by recent historians of ancient art as an episode, albeit one that lasted a good number of centuries, between periods of purely Greek art – the earlier Middle Helladic (2000-1600 B.C.) and the Geometric (end of the twelfth century to *circa* 700 B.C.) – an interlude that shook the permanent characteristics of the land, the rationalism and the style based above all else on the mean. While in Middle Helladic art the decoration is distributed architecturally over the surface of the vase, in the following Mycenaean period there suddenly appears a strange art, full of imagination and of whirls, with a sense of nature and perpetual change. Centuries had to pass before the old curvilinear decorative motif, the spiral, reappeared in Greek art. This motif, rolling gently and symbolising the eternal flow of life, and sometimes turning back on itself, was forgotten later in the Geometric period, when it was supplanted by the triumph of the rectangle, the large-scale meander. In the Mycenaean period, however, this motif, the spiral, swept all before it, together with others clearly based on plant life, like the rosette and the lily, or on marine themes, like the octopus and the nautilus. All the idiosyncrasy of Mycenaean form and of the arts practised by the men of that period – seal-engraving, fresco-painting, inlay work, embossed work, the arts of the goldsmith and the bronzesmith – would have remained unexplained, suspended amidst the serious Greek art and the scarcity of gold at that period, were it not for the fact that it is believed today that the Helladic culture was directly influenced by an earlier, rich and creative culture, which had a tendency to elevate nature and the whirl of the dance – that is the Minoan culture. This dependence on Cretan style and the Cretan way of life is clear, not only from the way of life and etiquette of the palace dwellers, but also from the very form of the art. As one gets to know the monuments better, it becomes slowly easier to distinguish the local element, which was not a joyful one, as in Crete, but serious and warlike. Dominant is the funerary character of the objects, which gave pleasure to the rulers of Mycenae during their life, and also accompanied them to the tomb.

Objects from the chamber tombs at Mycenae

In order to make things easier for the visitor, we begin our review not with the grave goods from the six shaft graves on the acropolis at Mycenae, but with other objects exhibited in the three showcases (**1-2** and **26**) to the right and left of the door. They were discovered between 1886 and 1889 by Chr. Tsountas, in 103 chamber tombs outside the acropolis, and they differ significantly from the finds of the older shaft graves. Gold is much scarcer here, and the large numbers of necklaces are made mainly from glass paste or other material, in imitation of the gold ones worn by the royal men and women. These tombs, cut into the rock, belonged to the families of the "urban" aristocracy who supported the power of the kings. On the basis of the finds, they are dated from the fifteenth to thirteenth century B.C.

No. 2971 Gold ring with a scene of
a "Sacra Conversazione"

Nos. 253, 254, 259 Three gold masks from Shaft Grave IV at Mycenae

No. 273 Gold rhyton in the shape of a lion's head

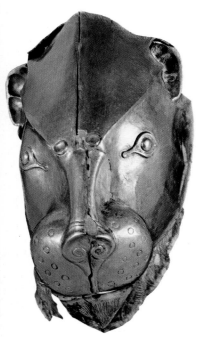

No. 241 Gold ring-seal with a scene of battle

No. 240 Gold ring-seal with a hunting scene

Case 26: Finds from the chamber tombs of Mycenae

The most famous of these grave goods is the one-handled silver cup, no. **2489**, with a frieze of inlaid and embossed male heads. They are of gold and black niello (a compound containing sulphur) affixed with borax.

Profile of a warrior, made of ivory (no. **2468**). He does not have a moustache, and wears a helmet covered with boar's tusks. The cheek-piece of no. **2470** is similar. No. **2490**. Pyxis of steatite, spherical, a relief octopus in the sea. No. **2257**. Clay pyxis with lid; painted birds.

No. **2262**. Small clay chariot with two riders. Cauldrons and vases of bronze, large and small. The large numbers of seal-stones in the two cases (26, 1) to the right and left of the door are made of a variety of precious stones: agate, onyx, sardonyx, steatite, jasper etc. The main subject used is a variety of animals of all kinds and sizes. Very fine work can be seen in the onyx seal no. **2439**, with the picture of a bull-leaper, superbly represented suspended in mid-air over the horns of an animal.

No. **2264**. Clay figurines of Mycenaean type, fourteenth-thirteenth century B.C. No. **2493**. Clay figurine of a *kourotrophos* from the thirteenth century B.C. No. **2491**. Egyptian faience vase with the cartouche of Pharaoh Amenophis III (1405-1370 B.C.).

Case 1: Finds from the chamber tombs of Mycenae

The gold rings are very precious; they are not as large as those from the shaft graves, but their motifs, in particular, contribute to our knowledge of religion. In most of the rings the decorated bezel is elliptical (nos. **2853**, **2971**, **2972**, **3148**, **3179**, **2852**, **2916**).

Case 2: Finds from the chamber tombs of Mycenae

Nos. **6523**, **6433**. Necklaces with beads of amber and other materials. Two clay female figurines with a small figure in the centre – holy trinity?

The six shaft graves on the acropolis at Mycenae, which filled this room with gold, were four-sided pits dug into the soft rock. They were surrounded by a double circle of vertical slabs of shelly limestone.

Case 27: Finds from Shaft Grave IV of Mycenae

Let us first examine the furnishings etc. of the richest tomb of all, the fourth (IV). The three gold masks (nos. **253**, **254**, **259**) have the facial features of three different types. All three are beardless; two of them are depicted with closed eyes and the eyelids engraved, and only in the third do the eyes seem to be open – though in fact they were closed. The mouth is outlined and the whole expression shows the peaceful contentment of death.

Much praise has been given to the gold cup from the tomb (no. **412**), on its high base like a communion chalice. There is a dove above each handle, stooping to drink, as in Nestor's cup (*Iliad* XI). The silver cup inlaid with gold, no. **390**, however, is more harmonious. It is decorated with gold leaves growing in a pot. The cup no. **440** stands out amongst the others because of its Greek simplicity and balancing curves. It has been considered the work of a Mycenaean goldsmith, not only because of its shape, which has affinities

No. 384 Silver rhyton in the shape of a bull's head with gold horns and a gold rosette on the forehead

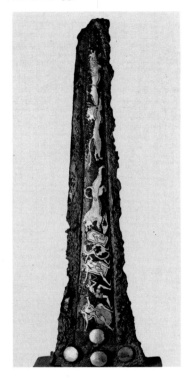

No. 394 Dagger from Shaft Grave IV

No. 294 Bronze dagger with a gold handle skilfully worked in cloisonnée technique

with the *kantharos* of later periods, but also because of its pure, ideal appearance. The same belief is not held in the case of two fine *rhyta* from the tomb. The gold one, no. **273**, has been superbly worked into the shape of a lion's head. The other rhyton, in the shape of a bull's head, is more impressive (no. **384**). This is silver with the high horns made of gold, and its internal core will have been of wood. A gold rosette is attached to the forehead, signifying that the animal has been dressed ready for sacrifice. The whole craftsmanship shown in both of them, and the presence of the bull, which has parallels in Cretan works, leaves no doubt that they were the work of Cretan smiths.

The earliest picture in Europe of a historical event is depicted on the silver Siege Rhyton, no. **481**. Only the right hand part of the repoussé picture has been preserved. The warriors are standing on rough ground and defending a walled city. Outside, to the left, are four trees, possibly wild olives. Of the defenders, only the archers and slingers are preserved, all of them naked; the former are kneeling while the latter stand. Below is the upper body of a warrior with a helmet, while outside the wall, the two men dressed in short chitons will be the elders, following the battle. On the towers of the wall, women make gestures of encouragement, and lamentation.

The theory has been put forward that a Cretan craftsman, serving in the Mycenaean palace, made this unique rhyton.

Nos. **241**, **240**. In Shaft Grave IV were found two of the most exceptional Mycenaean seal-rings. In the centre of the first towers a lone warrior facing three adversaries. On the second is a hunting scene with a two-horsed chariot.

On a separate stand: Daggers

Passing by the charming pedestalled gold cup, no. **351**, decorated with flowers, from the same tomb, we move on to the famous daggers. The more skilfully worked of them, no. **394**, was found in Shaft Grave IV. Three heavily-armed men are moving against an enormous lion, who has thrown their comrade to the ground. Two other lions are fleeing, startled, and one of them is looking backwards, thus forming a link with the main scene. The bodies of the men and of the lions are made of a mixture of gold and silver, and the shields are of niello. They are all colourfully inlaid into the smooth surface prepared for them, a technique which the ancients regarded as a gift from the gods.

Case 22 and 24: Finds from Shaft Grave IV of Mycenae

Also from Shaft Grave IV is the heavy bracelet, no. **263**, with the rosette in the centre, and the metal *rhyton* in the shape of a deer, no. **388**, an object imported from the East, like the gold shrine of the doves, nos. **242-244**, of fine metal.

No. **295**. Pommel cover; gold repoussé lion. The sword hilt no. **294**, which is cylindrical, with flowers in a polychrome cloisonné technique, is an unparalleled piece of work. It ends in a semicircle formed of two schematised dragon's heads. The inlaid stones are of azurite or crystal. The skilled hand of a Mycenaean craftsman at his best can be distinguished in the most elegant of the Mycenaean alabaster vases (no.

No. 624 The famous gold mask of "Agamemnon"

No. 625 Large gold breastplate

389, case 22). The curves of the body and the handles, and the furrows which relieve them, can only be explained in terms of the shape being copied from a bronze vessel. Nos. **245-7**. Three small gold pins. The large bronze swords from the tomb, are very fine. Large bronze vessels, vases and cauldrons (nos. **577, 582**) accompanied the dead in their tomb. Middle of the sixteenth century.

On a separate stand

No. **624**. We begin our description of the main grave gifts from Shaft Grave V with the much praised gold mask of "Agamemnon". It is the most expressive and perfect of the masks from Circle A. The face, by the hand of a skilled Mycenaean craftsman, is that of a true leader of men and king of kings. The craftsman will have known this face alive, in all its power, sagacious and severe, but mild when necessary. He will have known how to anticipate events and give orders, and undoubtedly also to be high-handed like the Agamemnon in the *Iliad*, Book I – because he felt himself to be the strongest, the "king of men", whom Zeus had made "distinguished amongst many and outstanding amongst heroes".

Case 3: Finds from Shaft Grave V of Mycenae

The representation on dagger, no. **765**, recalls a Nilotic scene, with its wild cat and papyrus plants. This is executed in the same technique as the other, drawing its inspiration from Egyptian motifs, which are rendered with a peculiar charm.
No. **744**. Bronze dagger inlaid with gold, with fine inlaid spirals that become progressively smaller towards the point. No. **855**. Large silver *oinochoe* with repoussé decoration. Broad spirals round the shoulder. No. **764**. Bronze dagger with gold handle, repoussé lilies. No. **812**. Square wooden *pyxis*. Above, attached faience dogs. No. **828**. Ostrich egg with applied faience dolphins. No. **689**. Necklace. The gold beads are in the shape of antithetic eagles.

Case 4: Finds from Shaft Grave V of Mycenae

Grave gifts, also from Shaft Grave V. The large gold mask, no. **623**, differs in its features from the others from Circle A. The broad face, without beard and apparently swollen, the small nose, and the large bare face, cannot be attributed to lack of skill on the part of the craftsman, for he has faithfully reproduced the features. In contrast with the Greek type of the other faces, one might say that this belonged to a man who was not a Mediterranean type, but who came from some tribe in the north-eastern area. The large gold breastplate, no. **625**, has repoussé decoration with patterns of spirals and interwoven leaves divided by horizontal lines into two parts, one above the other; it will have been laid on the breast of one of the three dead males from Shaft Grave V. Nos. **808-811**. Wooden, hexagonal *pyxis*, decorated with repoussé metal plates on the sides: hunting of a deer and an antelope by a lion, amongst some trees. The upper and lower plates have different compositions. The luxuriant ornamentation, and the suggestion of the forest attest the practised hand of a great Mycenaean metal-worker. Nos. **629, 656**. Gold cups with repoussé dec-

No. 1428 Funerary stele with relief decoration from Grave Circle A at Mycenae

Nos. 3, 5 Gold diadem from Shaft Grave III at Mycenae

Nos. 808-811 Hexagonal pyxis of wood with applied gold plaques

No. 75 Gold brooch in the form of a goddess

No. 35 Gold seal with a scene of a duel

No. 33 Gold seal with a scene of a man fighting with a lion

oration; spirals and running lions. No. **829**. Alabaster vase with gold rim and handle.

Three *stelai* (nos. **1427-1429**) of shelly limestone (a soft porous type), with hunting scenes, were erected above Shaft Grave V. In the best preserved of them (no. **1428**) the main relief is in a field with rows of spirals above it. It depicts a man standing in a light one-horsed chariot; he is stooping and holding the reins, and his large scabbard hangs from his waist. Another man is walking in front of him; he is naked and holding aloft a large sword. The engraving is unskilled, and the subject is depicted in low relief, without any attempt to render it plastically.

Case 23: Finds from Shaft Grave III of Mycenae

Three princesses and two twin children were buried in the third shaft grave, which was just as rich and had two impressive gold diadems (nos. **1**, **3**, **5**). We do not know whether or how the diadem was supported on the head of one of the women; this diadem can only be understood in terms of influence by the Minoan Palace Style. However, the Mycenaean metalworker has given a certain order, and almost geometric composition, to the pattern of rosettes. The crown of "funnels" above and around the edge of the main plate (no. **1**) is a schematised pattern of Minoan lilies. The second diadem (nos. **3**, **5**) is almost barbaric in form, with large elliptical, pointed rhombuses above the main plate; both these and it are decorated with circles. The corpse of the dead princess must have seemed very splendid with such a weighty crown on her head!

There are a great number of small pieces of gold foil, distinctive among which, as offering evidence for religious practices, are the two small pieces nos. **27-28**, with the naked goddess (Aphrodite?) surrounded by doves; and particularly no. **26**, with the façade of a triple shrine; sacred horns at the centre and doves at the sides indicate the presence of a goddess. The pair of gold earrings, no. **61**, and especially the large silver pin, no. **75**, are masterpieces of the goldsmith's art; the latter has a gold plate attached to one side: above the head of a goddess are supported two plant ornaments, one above the other, from which the rich leaves and flowers that enclose her branch out. This wonderful picture represents the deification of a protectress of the plant world, of Spring and of the rebirth of life.

One of the two other pins from the grave, nos. **102**, **103**, has a large head of rock-crystal, and the other, smaller one, has a similar double head. No. **35**. Square gold seal with a scene of a duel. No. **33**. Similar one: a man fighting with a lion. No. **34**. Fine picture of a lion falling (wounded?) from a rock. No. **116**. Sard; duel. Nos. **2**, **8-14**, **16**, **18**, **20**. A large number of gold leaves – about 700 were found in Shaft Grave III.

Cases 28-29: Finds from Shaft Grave III of Mycenae

On the table in the middle is the almost chilling sight of the gold images that covered the two young children. The schematised mask of one has survived (no. **146**). The dark legends of the Atreidae disturb the mind of the visitor.

Two small scales, nos. **81-82**, are generally believed to symbolise the weighing of the soul in the Underworld. Nos. **72-74**, **83-85**. Small, simple gold vases, two *pyxides*, etc. from the women's quarter. Nos. **25**, **86-88**, **62**, **89**, **90**. Crosses consisting of four gold leaves of different sizes, with repoussé circles and two bronze nails in the centre to attach them.

Case 22: Finds from Shaft Graves IV and VI of Mycenae

The oldest shaft grave, the sixth, which was excavated by the ephor Stamatakis, was poor in grave goods but contained a large number of dark coloured pots typical of early Mycenaean art. Nos. **946**, **947**. Beaked jugs of island style. Two or three large birds are painted on the spherical body.

On a separate stand near case 3

No. **948**. Large amphora with griffin facing right. The body is outlined and painted white.

The vases from Shaft Graves I, II (case 25) and III (cases 23, 28, 29) are also worth noting, since they are representative of early Mycenaean pottery, in particular the slender jug from Grave I, no. **199** (case 25); this has ivy tendrils harmonising with the shape of the vase. It is worth emphasising that it was above Shaft Grave II that the poros stele with the snakes was erected (no. **1430**).

Cases 5, 6: Finds from Grave Circle B of Mycenae

A second grave circle was discovered by chance in November 1951, outside the acropolis at Mycenae to the west, and was excavated in 1952-55 by J. Papadimitriou. Twenty-four tombs were discovered. Apart from a large number of pots (most of them in the Nauplion Museum), the grave gifts consisted of bronze knives and swords. In the case of no. **8710** (case 6), an exceptionally long one, the gold covering over the hilt has also been preserved. Gold drinking vessels, diadems and bracelets were also found. Nos. **8635-8637** (case 5). Three bronze pins with heads of rock crystal. The charming small vessel no. **8638** (case 5), in the shape of a duck, is made of the same material. The small amethyst seal, no. **8708** (case 6) with a male head, furnishes invaluable evidence for the appearance of the Mycenaeans. No. **8709**. Death mask, with a dull appearance because it is made of electrum, an alloy of gold and silver. On the basis of the pottery, some of the tombs are dated to a period earlier than that of the six shaft graves of Circle A inside the acropolis.

Case 7: Finds from the tholos tombs of Mycenae

A small part of Grave Circle B was cut into by a *tholos tomb*, which has been called the *"tomb of Clytemnestra"*. The grave gifts were found in the *dromos* of the tomb. The body of a woman had been laid there in an uncovered pit, and, as the excavator of the tomb, Tsountas, believed, she must have "died at the same time as one of the lords". The bronze mirror, no. **2898**, with the fine ivory handle undoubtedly belonged to her. Two women with foreign faces (Ethiopians?) are sitting face to face on the trunk of a palm tree, stooping so as to fit into the shape of the handle.

The development of Mycenaean power and the diffusion of Mycenaean culture began earlier, in the fourteenth century, when Crete became subject to the Achaeans. Immediately after 1350 B.C. they fortified the acropolis with the gigantic "Cyclopean" walls. The Lions' Gate – those protectors and representatives of the king's power – shows a tendency to monumental architecture that was never known on Crete. It may have been while he was still alive that the king who

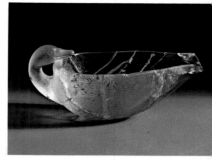

No. *8638 Vase of rock crystal in the shape of a duck. From Grave Circle B*

No. *8708 Small seal of amethyst. From Grave Circle B*

No. 7711 Ivory figurine

No. 992 Gold ring with a cult scene

girded the acropolis with the Cyclopean walls ordered the building of his tholos tomb – the Treasury of Atreus, as it was known in the time of Pausanias.

The new Cyclopean wall did not harm the earlier six royal shaft graves; at this same period they were surrounded with a single circular perimeter wall, as though they were a holy and inviolable sanctuary. It appears that the grave *stelai* were re-erected then as unforgettable tokens that royalty was buried there.

Case 21: Finds from the acropolis of Mycenae

At the same period, immediately after the middle of the fourteenth century B.C., the new palace, the Megaron, excavated by Tsountas, was built high on the crest of the acropolis. Some of the finds are very valuable for dating purposes – the faience figurine of a monkey, no. **4573**, with the cartouche of Amenophis II (1450-1423 B.C.), and two small faience plaques with the remains of the cartouche of Amenophis III (1405-1370 B.C.).

No. **2666**. Limestone block with cult scene. In the centre is an armed goddess (Palladion), framed by a woman who is worshipping her. No. **2665**. Remains of a fresco. Deities with asses' heads are holding poles, and perhaps animals of the hunt will have been hung from the ends of them.

The granite mould (no. **1018**) was found in a house on the acropolis in 1890. On both sides it has moulds for the hammering of ornaments in gold, or for casting them in glass paste.

On separate stands

The belief that there never existed any Mycenaean monumental plastic art is partly refuted by the plaster head, possibly of a Sphinx (no. **4575**). On the white coat, the curls, eye brows and eyes are painted in black, and the fillet around the low forehead, the lips and a mark (perhaps tattoo) on the cheeks and chin are in red. The head has an other-worldly expression (fourteenth to thirteenth century B.C.). Stele no. **3256**, of sandstone with incised decoration, would have stood originally on an earlier grave of the sixteenth century B.C. It was later covered with lime plaster and painted in three registers. In the widest, middle register, five warriors marching right. They each hold a round shield in the left hand and brandish a spear in the right. The painted stele probably dates from *circa* 1200 B.C. and seems to copy the same prototype as the Warrior krater, no. **1426**.

Case 30: Finds from the lower city of Mycenae

Important works of art give a noble appearance to the case in the centre. The ivory figurine, no. **7711**, with the two goddesses and the "divine child", came to light in the excavation by Wace in 1939, and astonished everyone by its craftsmanship and its religious significance. Wearing Creto-Mycenaean dress, they have their arms around each other and are protecting the small child between them. A wonderful cloak is worn by both goddesses, whom we may perhaps venture to call Demeter and Kore. Fifteenth century B.C. In the same case are the headless ivory figurine of a seated female, no. **5897**, and the bronze statuette, no. **2631**, which was imported from the East. The main attraction in this case, however, is the "treasure" of two gold rings (nos. **992-993**) and four gold cups (nos. **957**, **958**, **959**, **960**). The very fa-

No. 4575 Female head in plaster (Sphinx?)

Nos. 8339, 8340 Bronze daggers from a tomb at Myrsinochori, Messenia

mous and greatly praised gold ring, no. **992**, has an elliptical bezel, with a rich and precious engraved scene. A goddess is sitting under a tree; opposite her are standing two women dressed alike. Between them, on high, is an idol in full armour, and two female figures – attendants; on high, there is also a double axe, and the heaven with the sun and half moon. Tsountas thought the idol was a representation of Zeus. The solemn seated goddess can only be given the general designation of goddess of nature, or Mother Earth. No. **993**. Gold ring from the ame treasure. Six animal heads in two rows, one above the other, bucrania and lions' heads. The two gold *kylikes*, nos. **957**, **958**, with handles ending in dogs' heads, have distinctive harmonious curves. From the same treasure come the other two, nos. **959**, **960**, and also no. **961**, which has only one handle. The small couchant lion, no. **991**, of solid gold, will have been attached to the rim of a vase. Nos. **962**, **974**. Gold "hair-pins".

Case 31: Finds from the lower city of Mycenae

No. **7387**. Large fragment of a krater with chariot. The subject and style are the same as others from Tiryns, Cyprus and the East. The couple on the chariot are barely distinguishable and it is uncertain whether the scene is mythological.

The recent finds from houses in the lower city at Mycenae afford evidence for the specialisation of Mycenaean craftsmen in the art of working ivory. Most of the objects, from the "House of Shields" were inlaid in chests or other furniture (no. **7401** etc.) of the thirteenth century B.C. Similar ivory plaques were discovered by Wace in the "House of the Sphinxes", some having sphinxes on them, and a few with Linear B script, like that of Pylos. No. **7386**. Clay rhyton with a painted octopus from the "House of the Wine-Merchant". Fourteenth century B.C.

On a separate stand: The Warrior krater

Still at Mycenae, a picture of the difficult times that began in the twelfth century, when the Mycenaeans began to fear other peoples, is offered by the Warrior krater, no. **1426**, which was discovered outside Grave Circle A. On the front are six warriors, each armed with a short shield and spear and wearing the chiton and a short breastplate; they look menacing in their helmets, and are departing towards the right for a campaign. At the side, a woman raises her hand in a gesture of farewell. She wears black, instead of the earlier patterned dress – a sign of a change produced by fear.

The Palace of Nestor

Case 8: Finds from the Palace of Nestor and tombs in Messenia

There is no doubt today that the Mycenaean palace discovered by Carl Blegen on top of the hill of Ano Englianos in Triphylia is fit to be described as the Palace of Nestor, the wordy old warrior of the Homeric poems.

Amongst the finds in the palace we may distinguish the ten heads of unshaven bearded men, no. **7842**, made of gold and niello; they will have been inlaid on a metal vase.

Let us first examine the grave gifts yielded by the excavation of a

No. 7986 Precious square gold bead from the Palace of Nestor at Pylos

No. 1426 The famous Mycenaean "Warrior krater"

tholos tomb at Myrsinochori, north-east of the Palace of Nestor. The dagger, no. **8339**, is decorated with one of the most charming pictures in inlaid technique: nautiluses are inlaid in gold on the blade, getting progressively larger towards the handle. The other dagger, no. **8340**, has been preserved together with its gold handle. Above, in the centre, are animals amongst bushes. Six or seven dead had been buried in a pit. A necklace, no. **8356**, with beads of amber had been put round the neck of the man buried last in the tholos, and a large number of seal-stones were found in the pit (second half of the sixteenth century B.C.), some around the abdomen of the dead man buried in the tholos, and four in the position of the right hand (date of the latest, 1500-1430 B.C.).

No. **8323**. Sard. A woman with naked breasts is hurrying to put two lilies on an altar. Above, between the double horns, are two olive branches. No. **8322**. Sard. Scene of two lions and behind them the torsos of two men. No. **8344**. Offering table painted with octopus.

The finds from three tholos tombs at Ano Englianos reveal both the wealth of the rulers of Messenia and the level of their art: ivory objects, beads, necklaces of amethyst, amber, faience etc.

The most important of the small finds are no. **7907** – four small gold owls – and a precious square gold bead, no. **7986**. On one side is a truly fabulous seated griffin with his huge wings spread out and a high crest. It will have had symbolic significance for the palace; there is a similar painted one in the small throne room at Knossos.

From the tomb at Kakovatos, Tryphilia: no. **5678** an ivory comb. No. **5662** a small owl. No. **5662** a little frog and a sheet-gold plaque.

Case 9: Clay tablets of Pylos

On a table by the wall is exhibited what is only a small selection of the most important movable finds from the excavations of the Palace of Nestor – the many hundreds of clay tablets with incised writing. 600 of these were discovered in 1939 in the first excavation of Kourouniotis-Blegen, and it was recognised that they were inscribed with the Linear B script, known from Crete. From 1952 on, hundreds more were discovered in the so-called "archive room" of the palace, immediately inside the main entrance. The tablets total about 1200, all of them black from the fire that destroyed the palace (but which also baked the clay); they must have been deposited only one or two years previous to it, for they all appear to be contemporary. In 1952 the English architect M. Ventris made an important breakthrough in the decipherment of these inscriptions, and established that the language of them is Greek. They are written in a mixture of ideograms and syllables, and are close to Arcado-Cypriote dialect. Today the reading of them has advanced greatly. They refer, in signs and letters, to agricultural products, such as olives, wine and honey, and also to the vessels collected in the royal store. We can also read the words for "king", "people", "Pylos", "cypress", "cup", 'tripod', and possibly some names of gods.

Case 32: Finds from the S. Peloponnese – Vaphio, Kambos in Lakonia and Kalamata

The *tomb of Vaphio*, a short distance to the east of Amyklai, Sparta, was first excavated in 1805. Many decades later, however, it was

Clay tablet from Pylos with incised Linear B script. From the Palace of Nestor

Nos. 1758, 1759 The two gold cups from the tholos tomb at Vaphio

No. 1770 Seal-stone of sardonyx

Tsountas, sent as ephor to Lakonia by the Archaeological Society, who first saw that the excavation of it should be completed. The reward for his conscientiousness was far from small; inside he found a veritable treasure of grave gifts: bronze vessels, swords, and six bronze knives, a ladle (strainer), a large number of sealstones, amethyst necklace beads, a dagger inlaid with gold, a silver *phiale* (drinking bowl), lamps, a bronze axe, etc. But the most fabulous gift of Fortune was the two gold cups (nos. **1758**, **1759**, outside the case on separate stands) with relief representations of bulls. No traces of the skeletons were found in the tomb, but Tsountas concluded from their position within the pit that one of the gold cups together with a second, simpler, silver cup and a heap of seal-stones, had been placed by the right hand. The other gold cup, three seal-stones and other stones must have been laid at the left hand.

The subjects and the craftsmanship of the two repoussé cups, which formed a pair, are unique. Their handles were made separately and attached afterwards to the main body.

Two contrasting scenes are shown in repoussé decoration on the cups. On one is the dangerous attempt to catch two half-wild bulls in a net whose ends are tied to two trees. In the centre of the other is the idyllic meeting of a bull and a cow. A bull-leaper in front has tied a thick rope to the foot of another one, and at the other side a third bull lowers its head and sniffs the ground. The artifice has been achieved by the presence of the cow, making it easier to take them. All the figures on both cups stand on the ground, and trees, leaves and rocks have also been depicted – the last as though suspended in the air, because the craftsman did not wish to render them in perspective. There can be no doubt that the skilled metal-worker was a Cretan. Perhaps they were a gift from a Cretan grandee to the king of the region, or perhaps they were ordered by him? We cannot know. The seal-stones found in the pit were made from a variety of precious stones: haematite, chalcedony, sard, onyx, sardonyx, jasper and agate. They are also dated to the fifteenth century B.C., and the cups may have been a little earlier.

No. **1801**. Gold ring with a scene depicting tree-worship. Of the seal-stones, on no. **1761**, of onyx, a representation of a priest holding an axe of Eastern type. No. **1789**, of sardonyx, an excellent spring picture of a dancing woman. No. **1770**. Sard, a light two-horsed chariot and two riders. No. **1768**. Agate, with an exceptionally fine seated lion. No. **1793**. Onyx, with two ducks.

In the same case are the finds from the tholos tomb at *Kambos* of Avia in Messenia (sixteenth to fifteenth century B.C.). The lead statuette, no. **3301**, is a local work, probably imitating a Cretan model. It has become generally known, wrongly, as the flute-player. No. **3303**. Chalcedony, with a gold setting of two goats. No. **8913**. Bronze statuette representing a male worshipper.

On a separate stand

The provenance of the statuette no. **6284** is unknown. It is of purely Minoan type, and has the Cretan movement that is missing from the other, Helladic, statuette from Kambos Avia (no. **8913**).

On the wooden partition: Frescoes from the palace at Tiryns

The walls of the second palace at Tiryns in the thirteenth century B.C. were decorated with a large colourful procession of women. The upper body of one of them, with naked breast, has been preserved

No. 5883 Head of a woman from a fresco showing a procession of women. From Tiryns

(no. **5883**); she will have been holding a *pyxis* in her hand. The lower part of the body is restored after a similar figure in the palace of Kadmos at Thebes. The white of her face and the naked parts of her body are enclosed by a black line against the blue background. While this procession was moving to the right, a corresponding one, of other women, moved to the left, and was probably the decoration from a different wall. Parts of the faces have been preserved, framed by beautiful black curls similar to those of the first figure; richer curls have fallen down to frame the body. Her face is very charming.

The other picture, of two women in a chariot, is connected with the boar hunt (see the other side of the partition). The figures are wearing simple dress which covers their breasts, and the first one is holding the reins. These ladies of the court, taking part in the hunt, are erect and "wooden", like the schematised leafless trees behind them. It is a colourful picture. The main scene of this fresco also has a blue background (nos. **5878** and **5882**); on one surface, above and below, are dogs, and in the middle the great boar, suspended in space, with most of his body a brown colour. Two spears have already pierced his head and back, and the end of the dark brown arm of one of the men holding the spear has been preserved.

Schematised trees wave in the wind behind the animals. The theme of the hunt is Helladic, but the ladies of the other fresco with the procession are curiously enough wearing the dress known from Cretan works two centuries earlier. The remains of the other fresco also have a Cretan theme, bull-leaping (no. **1595**). A woman, with white body against a deep blue background, is suspended above a bull, ready to tame him. It will have been modelled on similar splendid Cretan subjects. Nos. **5884-5885**. Fragments of frescoes of the earlier palace, *circa* 1350 B.C.: warriors.

Case 33: Finds from the tomb at Dendra (Midea, Argolid)

The contents of case 33 bring us back to the cradle and main centre of Mycenaean culture, the Argolid; it contains the precious grave gifts from the tholos tomb at Dendra (ancient Midea), which was without doubt a royal tomb. The large necklace with gold rosettes, no. **7342**, was worn by a princess buried in a pit in the tholos. Two skeletons were found in the main pit. The silver cup, no. **7336**, decorated with five bucrania of gold and niello, had been placed on the breast of the dead princess. On the king's chest lay the famous splendid gold *phiale* (no. **7341**), with repoussé octopuses and marine flora, a work so Cretan as to suggest the theory that perhaps it came from a raid by Achaeans on Crete about 1400 B.C. Rings and seal-stones were found in the bowl. Silver vases were discovered close by, and the bronze sword, no. **7325**, with an ivory pommel, and no. **7326** with a pommel made from precious stone was found on the right side of the king, while at his feet were swords, daggers, etc. No. **7337**. Ostrich egg. It had been made into a rhyton with a silver mouth and decorated with metal bands round it. The seal-stones, of onyx etc., are amongst the largest and most skilfully worked of the Mycenaean seals; they have pictures of animals. No. **7327**. Gold ring with picture of four animals in an unusual composition, separated by a horizontal line.

Case 13: Finds from tombs in Nauplion

Although they were so near to golden Mycenae, the tombs on the north-east slope of the Palamidi (1878-1880 and 1892) did not yield

No. 7337 Ostrich egg from the tomb at Midea in the Argolid

No. 6217 Small bronze wheels from Tiryns

No. 6208 Large gold ring from Tiryns. A seated goddess and procession of daemons

No. 6209 Gold ring from Tiryns. A ship and the abduction of a woman (?)

rich finds. In the chamber tombs, both in the *dromos* and in the niches, had been placed clay figurines of types *Φ* and *Ψ*, along with small gold ornaments, a number from glass paste, and a variety of other figurines of Late Helladic III date. The small clay chariot, no. **3492**, is very charming, though it has no rider.

On a separate base

On a separate base is the amphora, no. **5650**, from a tomb at Deiras, Argos. Two large aquatic birds in a very skilful composition on the two sides of the vase.

Case 12: Finds from the chamber tomb at Spata

The finds of case 12, from a chamber tomb at Spata, are not on display at present, pending completion of the exhibit of Mycenaean finds from Attica.

A number of tombs in Attica from the thirteenth century B.C. yielded a very small number of gold objects and rather more, and certainly more important, works in ivory. Case 12 contains some of these finds from a tomb in the village of Spata in the Mesogeia. Most of them were scattered near the entrance. Glass-paste ornaments abound. The ivory objects are particularly well executed. No. **2044**. An ivory comb with seated sphinxes and an elegant rosette in relief. No. **2055**. Half the head of a bearded warrior in profile, wearing a boar's tusk helmet. The hole indicates that it was attached to a piece of furniture or a vessel. No. **2051**. Square plaque with couchant sphinxes, their wings artistically spread forward and back. The differentiation of planes in the relief is exceptional. No. **2157**. A ring with agate bezel bearing a griffin.

Case 18: Finds from the tholos tomb at Menidi

A number of grave gifts were yielded by the excavation of a tholos tomb (thirteenth century B.C.) outside Menidi in Attica (Acharnes, on the site Lykotrypa, 1878).
No. **1984**. Cylindrical *pyxis*, with two rows of animals in relief around the body. On the lid a similar one, seated. The lyre, no. **1972**, with standing sphinxes on its base, is assembled from a large number of fragments. In the centre there is a column with a simple capital.

Cases 10, 11: Finds from Prosymna

There are a large number of not particularly valuable finds from other centres in the Peloponnese, mostly of pottery. A representative selection was yielded by the excavation of Prosymna, which became the Argive Heraion at a much later date. There were a few shaft and cist graves of the Middle Helladic period, and all the rest were chamber tombs. There are two swords in a poor state of preservation. No. **8446** (case 10) has inlaid dolphins of gold and niello on both sides. Fifteenth century B.C. No. **6416** (case 11) is similar with remains of doves. No. **6633** (case 10). Offering table with 12 circular hollows painted with rosettes. The earliest pots of the excavation, from the Late Helladic I period, have a pleasant decoration of leaves (two rhytons etc.). The vases without gloss have a light linear decoration. The *kylikes* on high bases, also matt, have a noble shape, as does the Ephyrean *kylix,* no. **6948** (case 10), with the tresses decorating it waving in the wind. There are a large number of figurines representing the female deity. No. **7041** (case 10). Clay bed. No. **6580** (case 11). Small ivory figurine of a woman with naked breast. The seal-stones from the chamber tombs are comparatively few, but fine pieces of work. No. **6409** (case 11). Onyx cylinder. No. **6425a** (case 11). Rockcrystal. No. **6249**. Haematite. No. **7109**. Sard. No. **7110**. Agate: three deer. No. **6615**. Amethyst. No. **8455** (case 10). Gold ring. On the elliptical bezel, antithetical griffins with a stele between them. A large number of steatite buttons, necklaces of glass paste, and beads.

On the table

The large amphora, no. **6725**, is Palace Style with a rich theme of three octopuses and seaweed – a Cretan motif reworked by a local potter.

Case 15: Finds from Tiryns

The *treasure of Tiryns* does not come from the excavation of a palace or of tombs. A workman found it by chance on the 21st December, 1930, buried in the ruins of what later proved to be a Middle Mycenaean house. All the precious objects, seized on a plundering raid, had been put in the large bronze cauldron no. **6226a**. Of the bronze objects, no. **6224**, a cup, has a certain grace; there is a bird sitting on its rim. No. **6228**. Two bronze knives of northern type. No. **6228a**. Iron, sickle-shape. No. **6217**. Two circles made of coiled wire, with pierced pieces of amber in the middle of them. No. **6219**. Two wheels with crosses in the middle; here also, pieces of amber are attached to the spokes. No. **6225**. Bronze tripod from a cauldron; the legs are flat in section and end in spirals at the top. Above, between them, birds hang from rings. Round cross-spokes between the legs served to strengthen it. No. **6208**. This is the largest ring known in the Mycenaean collection and is made of gold foil wrapped round an iron core. A scene of a fertility rite is engraved on the heavy elliptical bezel. Four daemons, with the body and head of a lion, each holding an *oinochoe,* are walking towards a goddess who is seated on a simple throne, with her feet resting on a footstool. She is holding a heavy conical vase in her left hand, and in front of her is a censer. A bird fills the space behind her back, and nature is depicted above – earth and plants, and the heaven with the sun and new moon. The other gold ring from this treasure, no. **6209**, though smaller, is interesting. On its bezel is an unusual picture of an "abduction" in front of a ship riding at anchor, which takes up half the picture. The miniature picture and figures are unusually small, and appear to be scattered at random. Two of the four largest figures are male and two female. In the smaller pair the man is putting his hand on the shoulder of the woman. Three oarsmen and two small male figures in the ship. No. **6214**. Syro-Hittite cylinder with a scene possibly from mythology.

It is difficult to date these objects with any accuracy, coming as they probably do from a raid on a palace. The tripod (no. **6225**) dates from the sub-Mycenaean period at the end of the twelfth century B.C., as does the ring (no. **6209**) with the scene of the "abduction".

Case 16: Finds from Skopelos

The large, valuable gold hilt (no. **6444**) was found neither at Mycenae nor at Pylos, but far to the north in a tomb in the south of Skopelos, at the site that is still today called Staphylos. In ancient times the island was under the domination of Staphylos from Crete. It is the

No. 6444 Sword hilt covered in sheet gold. From Skopelos

No. 8557 Rhyton in the shape of a winged shoe

Nos. 8844, 8088 Cylinder seals

largest sword known from the Mycenaean period, and will have been made after 1500 B.C. The repoussé handle is completely covered with decoration, chiefly of spirals, and its pommel is similarly covered with appliqué leaves.

Case 19: Finds from Attica: Salamis, Thorikos, Brauron, Markopoulo, Athens etc.

No. **8557**. Rhyton in the shape of a shoe with schematised wings. Its "point" is turned upwards. It was found in Attica, in a tomb at Halyki, Voula (1955), and is a significant masterpiece of both pottery and painting of the fourteenth century B.C. There is nothing to support the idea that it was connected with Nymphs etc. The vessel is better understood as being equipment for the dead man on his long journey.

In the pottery from the cemetery on Salamis (1893), near to Naustathmos, the complete mortification of the Mycenaean decoration is striking, as is the uniformity of the shapes and the small size of the pots. The predominant shape is the stirrup jar, nos. **3621**, **3616**, **3608**, of the eleventh century B.C.

Case 20: Finds from Attica: Perati

The grave gifts from the chamber tombs at Perati, a hill above Porto Rafti, illustrate well the uninspired nature of the decoration, and the monotony and poverty of Attic pottery in the thirteenth century B.C. The dating is established firmly by two cartouches of the Pharaoh Rameses II (1290-1224 B.C.). Nos. **8086**, **8087**. The most predominant shape is that of the stirrup jar. The two-handled bowl no. **9143** is an exception. Four clay figurines of women, lamenting with their hands on their heads, are attached to the rim of the pot at intervals. The decoration of the pots is linear and unemphasised, with the exception of the octopus, albeit schematised. Twelfth century B.C. Nos. **8265**, **8276**, **8277**. Fiddle-shaped clasps of the thirteenth century B.C. Two eastern cylinder seals, a few seal-stones, tools, a large number of minor objects in gold and silver, a lance, a bronze sword, bronze figurines etc.

Frescoes from Mycenae

The discovery by G. Mylonas in 1970 of this piece of a large-scale fresco in a house in the west wall of the acropolis at Mycenae, shed much light on the monumental painting of the thirteenth century B.C. No. **11670**. The female figure is depicted with the upper body full frontal, which gives her a certain divine appearance. The white face is painted on a deep blue background and her gaze is firmly fixed on the object she is holding tightly in her right hand In front she is touching her throat with her long fingertips. The ornaments, with their light colour, are empasised by the colours of her dress – brown, purple and white. The exquisite, very Greek face, is lost in thought. She has arbitrarily been called "Eriphyle", but an objection to this is that the as yet undeciphered, snake-like object does not resemble a necklace. However, one might claim that the figure of a tragic heroine is depicted in this unique picture.

Unique fragment of a fresco with a female figure: the "Mycenaean Lady" – Fresco with figure-of-eight shields. From the acropolis of Mycenae

Sculpture

ROOM 7 (First room of Archaic sculpture)

The origins of monumental plastic art

It was at a relatively late date that the Greeks began to set up in temples statues made of stone, limestone and marble. Earlier in the Geometric period, when the first temples were built on the sites of the Mycenaean palaces, the objects of worship were wooden statues erected in the inner sanctuary. The still grandeur of these is called to mind by a number of small ones that have survived (Heraion, Samos).

The craftsmen gave life, movement and expression to the type of the Classical goddess, at the same time freeing the statues of the youths from the support which, in the case of the Egyptian statues, hid the back of the body. They also erected in shrines and on tombs statues of seated revered goddesses made of stone or marble.

No. **804**. *Geometric amphora from the Dipylon*. The Geometric amphora from the Dipylon, the oldest and most monumental "statue" in this room, was a funerary monument. This proud art form and wonderful pottery technique did not emerge suddenly. The Geometric style developed throughout the whole of Greece, and with greatest effect in Athens, from the eleventh to the eighth century B.C., the period of the vase, until it gradually achieved the grandeur of the amphoras and kraters of the eighth century. The main motif is the meander which winds around the neck; the same decoration, running in the opposite direction, is dispersed intelligently and sensitively over the whole body of the vase, the main scene falling between the handles: the corpse lies on the bed surrounded by standing mourning figures, with other figures below the bed. The painters have not yet learned to distinguish male from female figures.

This monument will have stood on the tomb of some Athenian aristocrat above the urn that contained his cremated bones. It was made by an excellent vase-maker and painted by the "Dipylon painter", and is an impeccable early expression of the haughty Greek intellect and sense of symmetry and style.

No. **776**. *Ivory statuette of a naked goddess*. The skill of the Greeks at rendering the human form is demonstrated by an ivory statuette from a tomb in the Dipylon. The smaller ones found with it were eastern "wooden" works. One of them, with a *polos* on its head, was the main model which was transformed by an Athenian craftsman into a form with graceful curves; he also gave it a litheness and a lively expression, with eyes opening wide onto the outside world. *Circa* 750 B.C.

No. **1**. *Artemis of Nikandra*. This first statue listed in the catalogue of the National Museum was discovered on Delos in 1878.

Many centuries after the period of the Cycladic figurines in the Bronze Age, the people of the Cyclades turned again to carving marble and made their contribution to the creation of the monumental plastic art of the seventh century B.C. The female statue, its legs joined together, is a solemn figure without movement. The dress, which has no folds, was once decorated with colours. We are informed by the inscription incised on the left side that it was dedicated to Artemis by Nikandra of Naxos "outstanding above other women", as she emphasises with unconcealed pride. A Naxian work of 660-650 B.C.

No. **57**. *Statue of a seated kore or goddess*. The seated *kore* from Aghiorghitika in Arkadia is made from local stone, and depicts a goddess or a dead woman. The parts of the body are differentiated; the shoulders are rounded, and the head and upper part of the body are turned to the left, giving it life. *Circa* 630 B.C.

No. **2869**. *Carved head from a metope*. The carved head from a metope from Mycenae, which is one of the most expressive products of the so-called "Daedalic style", is dated to the middle of the seventh century B.C. This style originated in Crete and crossed to the Peloponnese, where local sculptors strove to imitate it. One would consider the head a Cretan, if not Corinthian, product, judging by the full face, the wide eyes and full lips of the goddess (?).

No. **56**. *Grave monument*. This early Boeotian grave monument of local limestone engages our warm sympathy. It depicts unskilfully in relief two statues of young men in the stance of *kouroi* embracing each other. *Circa* 560 B.C.

ROOM 8 (Second room of Archaic sculpture)

This room, like the others housing Archaic sculpture from the end of the seventh century to the beginning of the fifth century B.C., ex-

No. 804 Monumental Geometric amphora from the Dipylon

hibits great variety: statues of young men (*kouroi* as this category was first called), *korai*, in much smaller numbers, grave reliefs, sphinxes, a great variety of heads, fragments of statues etc., all coming from tombs or sanctuaries. The traces of colour that have been preserved show that the people of the Archaic period took delight in using lively colouring to cover the cold white marble. The type of naked youth, or *kouros*, was based on foreign models, and it constituted "an inspired misinterpretation of Egyptian models" (Buschor). It was developed by the sculptors of Ionia and the Cyclades and, at the same time or immediately afterwards, by the Athenians, all of whom ventured to depict their young men naked and without any supporting pillar. In the National Museum it is possible to study all the phases of the development of the subject: how the sculptors of the "latent movement" progressed from the end of the seventh century B.C. The tendencies of several workshops of Attica, the Cyclades and Boeotia are also represented here. The beginnings and the end of the *kouros* can be studied here, as nowhere else, in countless examples; the particular characteristics and formal development of the relief grave *stelai* are also illustrated.

No. **3645** *Large than life-size torso of a kouros (Dioskouros?)*. It had been erected in front of the earliest temple of Poseidon at Sounion. 600-590 B.C.

No. **3372**. *The "Dipylon head"*. Only the head and hand have been preserved of the colossal *kouros* from the Dipylon, the oldest known. It was erected on the tomb of a young man who met with a premature death. The height of the forehead is very striking, as is the development in depth of the face, the enormous ear and the wide open eyes. The neck is strong, and the necklace will have been of gold. On the forehead, above the "ringlets" of the hair-style, and above the ears, a broad band circles the head, to be tied at the rear in a knot. *Circa* 610 B.C.

No. **2720**. *Kouros from Sounion*. The colossal *kouros* from Sounion was the work of another craftsman; it was not a funerary statue but a dedication in the temple of Poseidon. Next to it are the two bases of *kouroi* which stood next to each other (nos. **3645a** and **3939**). The torso of another *kouros* (no. **3645**), a more complete work by the same sculptor that stood in the same sanctuary, has an attractive contrast between the plastic elevation of the chest and the linear rendering of the divisions of the abdomen. The schematic rendering of the hair in the two *kouroi* from Sounion dates them to a period slightly later than the *kouros* from the Dipylon. *Circa* 600 B.C.

No. **353**. *Amphora from Piraeus*. The large black-figure funerary amphora from Piraeus (or from Athens) is dated to about 590 B.C. The shape is noble and harmonious and it stands on a conical base. The main scene, in black-figure in the interior of the vase, symbolises departure; standing in a chariot (the horses are "wooden" in the old style) the dead man sets out on his long journey.

No. **15**. *Kouros of Ptoion*. The sharp execution of this limestone *kouros* head has been interpreted in recent decades as deriving from a tradition of wood carving. It comes from the sanctuary of Apollo

No. 3372 The "Dipylon head"

Ptoios (1885) and is merely a provincial work deriving from earlier Attic models. *Circa* 580 B.C.

Nos. **4** and **3443**. *Statuettes of women*. These marble *perirrhanteria* made charming dedications in the temples; the open bowl is supported by three female figures. The two small female figures, one more completely preserved, are the remains of a similar one found in the Boeotian shrine of Apollo Ptoios. End of the seventh century B.C.

No. **5**. *Headless statue of a kore*. The small statue of a *kore,* discovered long ago at Eleusis, has a simple technique. The body is flat in front and curved behind. The ends of the belt hang down in front below the overhanging fold of the Doric peplos. *Circa* 570 B.C.

ROOM 9 (First small room containing Archaic works)

No. **21**. *Statue of a winged Nike*. This Nike is one of the oldest finds on Delos (1877). The winged "messenger of the gods" is flying in the "unnatural" conventional Archaic style, and is excellently rendered. The Nike would have formed the *akroterion* on the pediment of an ancient temple. It is a charming work of about 540 B.C., by a Chian or Naxian, rather than a Parian, sculptor.

No. **1558**. *Kouros from Melos*. The Cycladic ideal of a *kouros* finds its expression in this work from Melos in the first of the small rooms; the arms hang lifelessly, the shoulders are weak, and the whole body is tall and slender, while the smile, which never lights up the faces of the Attic *kouroi* (an opening out towards life) is beautifully combined in this work with a sweet dreamlike isolation. 560-550 B.C.

No. **1586**. *Head of a kouros*. The large *kouros* head, which is also from Melos, suggests that, like the *kouros* no. **1558**, the torso will have been larger than life-size. 560-550 B.C.

No. **22**. *Statue of a kore*. This striking headless *kore*, an old find from the excavations on Delos, is also a Cycladic product. It is the same type as the Acropolis *korai*, and all the folds are worked in front, the rear view being neglected. Parian work of the last quarter of the sixth century B.C.

Nos. **3858**. and **11**. *Torsos of kouroi*. After viewing two *kouros* torsos, no. **3858** from Moschato in Athens which is two or three decades later than the Sounion *kouroi* with the long thin face and high forehead, and the delicately sculpted kouros torso from the Ptoion in Boeotia (no. **11**), which is a Cycladic work of about 570 B.C., the visitor is dazzled by the entrancing sight of Phrasikleia.

No. **4889**. *Phrasikleia*. The statue of Phrasikleia is a rare gift from the Attic soil; it was found almost embracing the statue of a *kouros* (no. **4890** in Room 10) and was also accompanied by an inscribed base, into which it has been successfully and certainly fitted, which gives us not only the name of the *kore*, but also, on the narrow side, that of the artist: "Aristion of Paros made (me)". This explains to some degree the unique nature of this *kore* in the series of Attic k*orai*. She is wearing the Ionic chiton, which she is holding with her right hand,

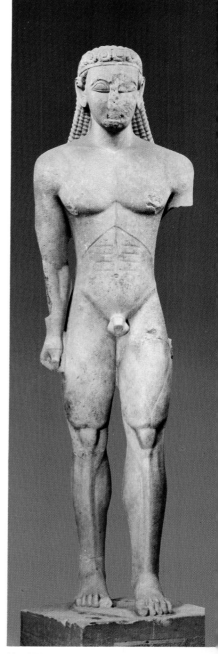

No. 2720 The Sounion kouros

47

while in the other she clutches a flower. The vertical edge of the dress which falls down from the neck is divided in the middle by the belt; it is interrupted only by the bosom of the chiton. Rosettes and meander-like rectangles are scattered here and there on the chiton, which is enlivened also by incised decoration. Tongue decoration forms the lower horizontal edge of the dress.

The sculptor will have known Phrasikleia alive and, one might well believe, will have seen her dressed in funerary garments as the bride of Hades. This is the complaint expressed in the inscription, that the gods had destined her to bear always the name of maiden. *Circa* 540 B.C.

ROOM 10 (Second small room containing Archaic works)

No. **2687**. *Stele of the Doryphoros* (youth carrying a spear). The tall slender stele of a young man carrying a spear is one of the oldest Attic grave *stelai* of the sixth century B.C., dating from about 560. It was discovered built into the Themistoklean wall in the Kerameikos, and had been dressed specifically for this purpose. The Gorgon below it, arranged like a metope, is better preserved and attests the quality of the whole work. A sphinx, symbolising death, will have stood on the top of the stele. *Circa* 550 B.C.

No. **38**. *The Discophoros* (youth holding the discus), from the Dipylon. There is a very illuminating fragment of a similar stele from the Dipylon, depicting a smiling youth holding a discus. The stele undoubtedly stood above his tomb. The moulding and the chisel work in the powerful face reveal the hand of a master sculptor. The face stands out in front of the discus, and the knot of hair, secured low down with pins, falls behind it onto the back. Work of the "Rampin" sculptor. *Circa* 560 B.C.

No. 38 The "Head of the Discophoros". From the Dipylon

No. **1541**. *Stele of a youth carrying a spear*. The fragmentary state of preservation of the Archaic Attic *stelai* in the Museum is compensated for by a discovery of recent years, the stele of the youth carrying a spear. We may overlook the excessive roundness of the back and concentrate on the quality of the carving, especially the attractive curls, which call to mind the description of the hair of the fallen Euphorbos: "hair like the hair of the Graces, and his tresses that were braided with gold and silver" (*Iliad* XVII 51-2).

No. **2891**. *Statue of a Sphinx*. Attic grave *stelai* were surmounted by sphinxes from about 600 B.C. until after the middle of the sixth century when they were replaced by the *anthemion*. The three in this room illustrate the three stages in the development of the form. No. **2891**, from the Kerameikos, is the work of a good sculptor, and has its arched wings (formerly coloured) spread out to an exaggerated extent; it is one of the first whose face is lit up by a smile. *Circa* 550 B.C.

ROOM 10

No. **1906**. *Kouros from Volomandra*. The slender funerary *kouros* from Volomandra in Attica has the form well known from the black-figure vases that were early works of the Amasis painter about 550-540 B.C. The sculptor has concentrated all his art in the face, lit by a smile, and the flame-like curls above the broad open forehead. Although the rendering of the arms is inferior, he knew how to set up his work solidly.

No. **4871**. This *kouros* head from a private collection is shown to be slightly earlier than the *kouros* from Volomandra by what remains of the three-dimensional modelling of the face. A band above the low forehead divides the curling locks into two, and gives the face an unusual grace. It is made by one of the earliest sculptors, possibly from the Cyclades. *Circa* 560 B.C.

No. **14**. *Torso of a kouros from Naxos*. The unfinished (half-worked) torso of a *kouros* from Naxos (1835) shows how the sculptors of the Archaic period worked the marble in the round separately at each stage of the carving, with a plastic sensibility which is missing in the late Hellenistic period. *Circa* 540 B.C.

ROOM 11 (Third room of Archaic sculpture)

No. **81**. *Pedestal of a funerary monument*. Only a part of the stepped pedestal with its plinth, and the incomparable toes, in sandals, are preserved from a *kore* who was wearing high sandals. The name of the sculptor ("Phaidimos made me") is incised in fine letters on the face of the highest step. Her name was probably Phile. *Circa* 550 B.C.

No. **61**. *Head of a kouros*. Near it on the wall, dominating the visitor's gaze, is the laughing head of a small *kouros*, turned distinctly to the right. The statue will have been erected somewhere in Eleusis. *Circa* 560 B.C.

No. **29**. *Funerary stele of the "Marathonomachos"*. The "Stele of the Marathonomachos" is in the tradition of the earlier Archaic grave *stelai*, and is one of the last before a law of about 500 B.C. prohibited their erection. It was discovered in 1839, together with its base, at Velanitheza in Attica, but it must date from 15 to 20 years before the battle of Marathon. It stood on the tomb of Aristion, whose name in the genitive is carved on the base. The name of the sculptor is carved below the feet of the hoplite on the projection: "The work of Aristokles". 510-500 B.C.

No. **13**. *Kouros from Megara*. The masterful *kouros* torso was discovered in Megara. It is later by some decades than the *kouroi* from Sounion (about 540 B.C.) plastic carving in the execution of the anatomy of the abdomen is more advanced and the arms are no longer of a piece with the body.

No. **3686**. *Kouros from Kea*. The body of the *kouros* from Kea (Tzia) is very strong for a youth and rather ill-suited to the charming, almost childlike face, which is "innocent and gay, but nonetheless looks on the world as though covered with a veil" (Buschor). *Circa* 520 B.C.

No. 1906 The Volomandra kouros

49

No. 29 The funerary stele of the "Marathonomachos", Aristion

No. **30**. *Stele of Lyseus*. This stele, on which the painting has been erased to the point where it is scarcely distinguishable, was found together with its base; a hexameter inscription on the latter informs us that this "mark" was set up for Lyseus by his father Semon. The galloping youth on the predella below can be distinguished better than the standing figure of Lyseus, the traces of which can hardly be made out. He is holding a *kantharos* in his right hand. End of the sixth century B.C.

No. **93**. *The Disc of Aeneas*. The "Disc of Aeneas" is unique amongst the sculptures. It is so named from the inscription carved around it: "This is the monument of the wise and excellent doctor Aeneas". Aeneas is depicted bearded and sitting on a simple chair facing right. *Circa* 500 B.C.

No. **86**. *Stele of Antiphanes*. Antiphanes, the name of the dead man, is carved in the genitive above this small simple stele. It was found long ago, together with its base, in Aiolou Street. 520-510 B.C.

No. **3072**. *Marble mask of Dionysos*. The marble mask of Dionysos was found at Ikaria in Attica, which to this day has retained the name "Dionysos" from the worship of the god. It was hung on a tree at the festival of "Dionysos of the tree" and crowned a body that was indicated by a striking chiton. 550-520 B.C.

ROOM 12 (Fourth room of Archaic sculpture)

Nos. **1933-38**. *Heads of warriors*. The Aeginetan heads in this room form an epilogue, though not the last, in the discovery of the sculptures of the temple of Aphaia, which took place during the Romantic period (early nineteenth century) and offered to the wide eyes of men the sight of the sculptures which subsequently adorned the Glyptothek in Munich. They are representative of the Aeginetan school and reflect works by the famous bronze-workers of the island in the years around 500 B.C.

No. **3711**. *Statue of a seated god*. The headless statue of a god seated on a simple stool (δίφρος ὀκλαδίας) is one of the most perfect pieces of Attic work of its period. Colours were used to enliven the panther skin and the cover of the stool, red being the predominant tone in the latter case. *Circa* 529 B.C.

No. **4797**. *Ionic capital*. The capital no. **4797** is a very important piece of evidence for the early form of the Ionic capital in Attica. It is a recent find from the region of Oropos and is an excellent piece of sculpture. It still has convex rather than concave spirals springing from a thick cushion (echinus) decorated with an engraved ornament.

No. **782**. *Anthemion of a funerary stele*. This is one of the most delicate of the *anthemia* from the Kerameikos which crowned the grave *stelai* of the Archaic period. It has out-turning petals and engraved members. The *anthemion* spreads out fan-wise above the two volutes, with nine petals, four either side of the central one. Other, smaller leaves are intertwined with the petals. End of the sixth century B.C.

No. **1959**. *Stele of the Hoplitodromos*. A central position is occupied by the much disputed "stele of the running hoplite", which has been known since 1902 (?) when is was discovered near the Theseion. Much has been written about the purpose of this work, discussion centering on the movement of it (which is based on the Archaic style), the graceful naked body, the helmet on the head, the stone itself, and finally the carving technique. As to the subject of it, the most attractive theory is the one recently put forward that it represents a man dancing the *pyrrhichios*. *Circa* 500 B.C.

ROOM 13 (Aristodikos room)

No. **3851**. *Kroisos*. The statue of Kroisos (in the large northern room) made of Parian marble and described on the inscribed base as a funerary statue, was discovered at Anavyssos in Attica. Of the three steps which the base will have had, only the front face of the middle one has survived, inscribed with its precious epigram.

The body is strong and fleshy, and the buttocks are emphasised in a reaction against the mid-sixth-century ideal of the slender *kouros*. A similar phenomenon in Athens can be observed in the figures of the vase painter Exekias. The hair falls in a curve on the back and curls charmingly at the sides and on the neck, and the curves of the arms have a similar gracefulness. The most probable dating for it is about 530 B.C., and it is not one of the latest of its type.

No. **9**. *Kouros from Boeotia*. The *kouroi* from Boeotia are provincial reflections of the Attic and Ionic *kouroi*, but they show a charming opening out towards life, with the exception of this clumsy mechanical product in Boeotian stone by a local mason from Orchomenos.

No. **32**. *Stele of Agathon and Aristokrates*. The stele and base, made from a single piece of marble, have the inscription (in anapaestic dimeters): "Monument to Agathon and Aristokrates" (two brothers?). *Circa* 500 B.C.

Nos. **12** and **20**. *Statues of kouroi from the sanctuary of Apollo Ptoios*. The statues found in the Ptoion, the sanctuary of Apollo, were dedicatory rather than funerary. The *kouros* no. **12** is the most representative, and already shows movement in the arms. Despite the roughness of the carving, the face has a pleasant light in it and the engraving of the anatomy of the abdomen is smooth. End of the sixth century. B.C. Another Boeotian *kouros*, the small, very graceful one from the sanctuary of Apollo Ptoios, is later than the end of the sixth century B.C. (no. **20**). The inscription incised on the thighs informs us that it was dedicated by Pytheas from Akraiphion and Aischrion to Apollo of the Silver Bow. The statue presumably depicts the god himself. *Circa* 500 B.C.

No. **3938**. *Aristodikos*. The statue of Aristodikos, a funerary statue, the last chronologically of the *kouroi* in the Museum, all of them Greek creations of the sixth century B.C. (This one will have been carved about 500 B.C.). It was found in 1944 by a villager from the Mesogeia in his field (the traces of the plough can still clearly be seen on the face) and brought to the Museum. "At an hour of great trouble it appeared from the soil of the fatherland to the light of day, some-

No. 30 The stele of Lyseus (drawing)

what larger than life size, with its powerful and slender youth, its restrained smile and its name, whose message echoed wide to lighten hearts that were oppressed" (Chr. Karouzos). It is made of Parian marble of excellent quality, and its plinth is also preserved (with the lead connection) along with the whole upper step of the base on which is incised the name (in genitive) of the dead youth: Aristodikos. The youth will have been the son of a noble family, and the statue will have fallen in the Persian invasion of 480 B.C.

No. **16365**. *Bronze Apollo*. It was possible to render the feeling of movement even more freely in the slighter bronze works. The very charming small Apollo, advancing with outstretched hand and his body leaning forward, represents the god at the moment of his epiphany. An outstanding Lakonian work. *Circa* 500 B.C.

No. **3476**. *Base with reliefs from a statue of a kouros*. The reliefs on the two bases which are shown by a hollow on the under-side to have been fitted onto a narrow pedestal, were not the work of the same sculptor. The three sides of one of them are carved in quite deep relief and represent athletic scenes from the life of a young man: wrestling, throwing the ball and running. The ball-throwing scene is excellently "balanced" by contrasting motifs. In the relief on the other side the youths are now dressed in himatia; two of them are seated and are setting a dog onto a cat, while two more are standing by and enjoying the game and laughing. The scene recalls the most beautiful of the Attic vase-paintings of around 510-500 B.C. The carving is striking, particularly in the rendering of the folds of the clothes.

No. **3477**. *Base with reliefs from a statue of a kouros*. The second square base, which was discovered together with the preceding one, is also adorned with reliefs on three sides. This is the work of another, more recent sculptor (500-490 B.C.). On the two sides are chariots with a charioteer and three hoplites, while on the central face young men are galloping and playing a game similar to hockey.

ROOM 14 (Room of Early Classical stelai)

No. **741**. *Stele from Larisa*. Non-Attic *stelai* are represented in this room but a number from Thessaly, of which the "stele with the hare" from Larisa is the most famous and the most interesting. It is unusually heavy and is preserved in its entirety, along with the *anthemion* that crowned it. A Thessalian youth, standing upright and dressed in a chiton and chlamys, and wearing a petasos on his head, is holding a hare in his right hand, and a piece of fruit in the other. *Circa* the middle of the fifth century B.C.

No. **739**. *Stele of Amphotto*. The Boeotian stele of the young girl Amphotto reveals the lack of movement typical of provincial tombstones. The girl's name has been inscribed in front of her face. The stele was discovered in 1890 outside Thebes. *Circa* 440 B.C.

Nos. **4478-79**. *Ionic capitals*. The two large capitals from the second temple of Athena at Sounion were first brought into this room

No. 1959 The stele of the Hoplito-dromos

Nos. 3851, 3938 Kouroi: Kroisos, Aristodikos

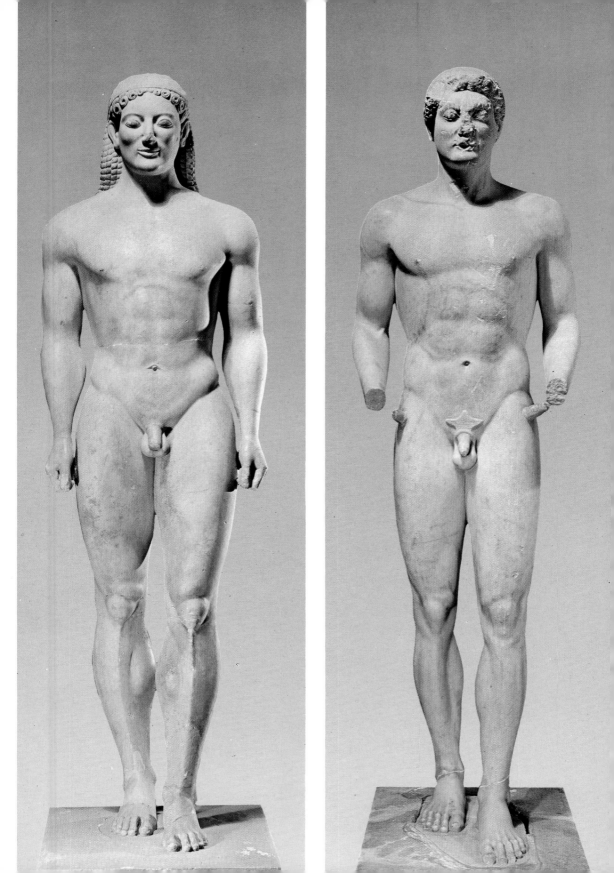

No. 3990 The "Melian disc"

No. 739 The stele of Amphotto.
From Boeotia

from an open courtyard in which they lay. The colouring is preserved only on the least complete of them, but in both of them the proportions of the volutes and the main shape of the column will have had an early, calm Classical balance. *Circa* 460 B.C.

The Severe style. The Severe style reflects the change of spirit that becomes clearer, on a pan-Hellenic scale, from 480 B.C. onwards, after the Persian wars.

The introduction of the Doric peplos, tied or not, instead of the Ionic peplos, which had been clearly associated in Athens with the period of the Tyrants, contrasts with the luxury of the Ionic dress. The expression on the face now becomes more concentrated and closed, and is no longer lit by the smile of the Archaic period; the introspective expression foreshadows the Classical art. Although it was based to a certain extent on the Dorian, Peloponnesian ideal, the technique of the Severe style achieved in Attica a grandeur and a spiritual depth of its own. Aeschylus, who was born at Eleusis in 525/4 B.C., took first prize in a dramatic contest for the first time in 484, and in 468 he came second to Sophocles; his first works, however, had already been produced in 500-490. Sophocles was leader of a victorious chorus as a young man after the victory over the Persians, but his first victory in a dramatic contest was won in 468 B.C. It was during these years that the great bronze-workers of the Peloponnese produced the majestic women dressed in the Doric peplos (*peplophores*). Very few copies of these have been found in Greece, in contrast with Rome, where the originals were transported after they had been plundered from the Greek cities. There, the Romans must have admired them greatly, and many of them will have ordered copies in marble.

No. **3990**. *The "Melian disc"*. The Severe style in the Cyclades is reflected by the "Melian disc". It is not known whether it stood in some temple of Aphrodite or on a tomb. The surface of the disc bulges towards the centre. The hair is tied behind with a "net", while in front of the ear and above the forehead, a gold plate will have indicated "golden Aprhodite". The branch of a plant, which most probably filled the empty space in front of her face and the carrying of flowers symbolised her as the goddess of birth, who bestowed fruitfulness and fertility, and even the hope of immortality. *Circa* 400 B.C.

No. **3344**. *Autostephanoumenos from Sounion*. We come to the Early Classical period in Attica with the "Autostephanoumenos" from Sounion; this is a dedicatory relief of a young athlete, probably from the temple of Athena there. The youth is naked and probably puts a metal crown on his head; his hair is short and his head bowed in silence out of respect for the deity. 460-450 B.C.

ROOM 15 (Poseidon room)

No. **126**. *Relief from Eleusis*. Wherever else other than in the Telesterion at Eleusis it may have been found, the large relief with the two Eleusinian deities can be imagined there. On the left is Demeter, majestic and priestly; her hair falls onto her back, and in her left hand

Nos. 3476, 3477 Relief bases from kouros statues. From the Kerameikos

she holds the sceptre, while with the other she is giving the ears of corn (once golden) to the naked youth Triptolemos. He is standing upright and listening to her orders to fly in his winged chariot and tell mankind about the great gift of the cultivation of the earth. On the right, and in contrast, is depicted the young Kore, Persephone. Unlike Demeter she is dressed not in the heavy Doric peplos, but in the light linen Ionic chiton and himation; she is holding the torch loosely in her left hand, while her right hand is laid in blessing on the young man's head. A local work. 440-430 B.C.

No. **1385**. *Relief of the horseman.* The heavy block with the simply carved relief of the horseman with a man standing behind him will have been a tombstone, possibly part of the monument of a dead heroised man.

As was said above, the type of the standing goddess wearing the Doric peplos was produced during the period of the Severe Style in the workshops of the bronze-sculptors of the north and central Peloponnese. The skilled craftsmen were inventive and moved towards the study of a factor which contributed to a new way of rendering the rhythm of the body, namely the balanced movement (*contraposto*), in which the relaxation of one leg is balanced by the stretching out of the other ("Spielbein" and "Standbein").

No. **1848**. *Headless statuette of a goddess.* The charming statuette from Rhamnous, which has unfortunately lost its head, is instructive for the lighter, Attic appearance of these *peplophores*. It was without doubt dedicated in the sanctuary there. *Circa* 470 B.C.

No. **1732**. *Akroterion-Hebe (?).* This full figure, representing the blowing of a sudden breeze, stood as an akroterion on the top of the tympanon of a temple in the ancient Agora; she is sent from heaven, and appears to be flying, though she does not have wings. It is the work of a skilled sculptor, and has been associated with the temple of Ares in the ancient Agora and interpreted as Hebe, a hypothesis which, though attractive, is unproven, *circa* 400 B.C.

No. **15161**. *The Poseidon of Artemision.* The hand of a large statue was discovered by divers from Trikkeri (north of Euboea) in 1926 at the bottom of the sea off Artemision, and later, in 1928, the bronze Poseidon was raised from the depths. It will have been seized by the Romans from a temple of the god, along with other works (the horse with the small jockey), but the god of the sea took his revenge and sank the boat which was going to unload it in a Roman harbour.

It is not only its height – 2.09 m. overall – that makes this a great work. The sculptor has captured the movement of the god, who is brandishing the trident (the open fingers exclude the possibility that the king of the gods was holding a thunderbolt). The achievement of the bronze-sculptor lies above all in the freedom with which he has rendered the legs wide apart, in chiastic balance with the open shoulders, and also in the working of the head, the curls on the forehead, and the hair tied behind in a charming plait. The elements that constitute the rhythm of the body are partly clear and partly obscure.

No. 3344 The "Autostephanoumenos" from Sounion

No. 126 The large Eleusinian relief, with the two goddesses and the young Triptolemos

The first scholar to interpret the work, Chr. Karouzos, proposed, with some reservation, that its creator was Kalamis, and he assigned it to the Sicyonian-Boeotian workshop. Another opinion assigns it to the Aeginetan sculptor Onatas. 460-450 B.C.

No. **45**. *The Omphalos Apollo*. It was Chr. Karouzos again who related the statue next to it, the "Omphalos Apollo", with the Poseidon of Artemision, putting forward the theory that it came from the same workshop. It derives its name from the Omphalos (the base of another statue, no. **46**), which was found close to it in the theatre of Dionysos in 1862. It is certain that this is a Roman copy, both from the workmanship and from the support behind the left leg. The famous original will have been of bronze, and will have been erected on some unknown spot about 450 B.C.

ROOM 16 (First room of Classical grave stelai)

The engraved marble *stelai* which stood on the Attic graves of the sixth century B.C., slender and enlivened with colour, were missing from the graves of Attica for over half a century. A law forbidding them, attested only by Cicero, crippled Attic art from 500 B.C. onwards. It is certain, however, that simple marble *lekythoi* or other monuments will have lightened the joyless world of the dead.

Relief funerary *stelai* reappear again from about 440 B.C., and the earliest of them are simple and humble. Two figures are usually depicted, one of them seated, though sometimes the relief has three figures, all standing. The engraving is in low relief, and the figures are rendered in a stiff, formal way. It is only later, with the influence of the sculptures of the Parthenon, that a restained grief appears in the face, and the figures become ethereal.

Grave stelai: no. **880** *of Kleomenes*, no. **712** *of Iphistiades*, no. **3845** *of Mnesagora and Nikochares*. Two of the oldest *stelai* from the fifth century B.C., that of Kleomenes (no. **880**, *circa* 440 B.C.) and the slightly more recent no. **712**, stand not so much side by side as slightly facing each other. No. **3845** is bigger, and depicts two young creatures who are named in the inscription on the simple epistyle. According to this, the parents of the two children set up the stele about 430 B.C. on the grave of Mnesagora and Nikochares somewhere in Anagyrous, Attica. The main figure is that of the sister, who is holding out a little bird to the small naked boy.

Nos. **37**, **4470**, **910**. *Island stelai*. There are some fragments of island *stelai*, including the torso of a youth from Kythnos (no. **37**), and the more charming one from Amorgos (no. **4470**), in which a seated woman is holding a writing tablet (430-420 B.C.). The influence of Cycladic *stelai* on the early Attic ones of the fifth century B.C. is attested by the fragment of a stele with the upper torso of a *kore* holding a *pyxis* from the women's quarters (no. **910**).

No. **715**. *Funerary stele*. The hand of an important sculptor who will have worked on the sculptures of the Parthenon — who other than the Parian Agorakritos? — is suggested by the funerary stele of a

No. 3845 Funerary stele of a sister and brother

No. 15161 The wonderful bronze statue, the "Poseidon of Artemision"

58

No. 715 Funerary stele of a youth

No. 4485 The lekythos of Myrrhine

youth and a small slave. The subject is unique and unprecedented, as is the size of the stele, at this period (*circa* 430 B.C.). The crowning member projecting above the figures is simple, with relief palmettes and lotus leaves – a scene filled with the deep significance of the rejuvenation of nature and man. There is a hint of death in the luminous figure of the youth on the verge of adolescence. A cat is sitting on a pilaster, and the upper body of a young naked slave is depicted *en face*.

No. **4485**. *The lekythos of Myrrhine*. The scene in relief is unusual. The figures stand on the ground which is only lightly indicated. Myrrhine goes forward, with her head held high and cloaked behind with the himation, allowing herself to be led by Hermes the Escorter of Souls. The two figures stand out, by virtue of their greater height, from three others lower down and to the left, which are well composed; the last on the left is a young man leaning with is elbow on a small column, and behind him is outlined the head of a young woman. The first of these figures is bearded and is holding out his hand as if to bid her farewell. He is most probably the father or the husband of Myrrhine, while the figures behind will be her mother and brother, or perhaps her brother and sister. Work of a somewhat mediocre sculptor. 430-420 B.C.

No. **2611**. *Grave stele of a Scythian archer*. The small stele with the inscription "Aristomedes set (me) up" is one of the humbler ones erected on the tombs of the poor, metics or foreigners. It was erected on the grave of a poor foreigner in the Kerameikos by a sorrowing acquaintance. The dead man will have been a Scythian archer, as the quiver depicted on it shows.

ROOM 17 (Room of Classical votive reliefs)

In the room between the first and second rooms containing Attic grave *stelai*, the most important and the finest votive reliefs are exhibited, along with others from the Argive Heraion which had an architectural function, and fragments from the temple of Nemesis at Rhamnous in Attica.

No. **2348**. *Akroterion from the temple of Nemesis*. The Parian artist Agorakritos carved the cult statue of Nemesis which stood in this last temple, and his hand is also to be seen in the large fragment from its main pediment. It shows the right foot of a woman standing on a plinth in the shape of a rock. Higher up are the foot and the remains of the lower leg of a man who is running to seize her – Boreas and Oreithyia.

No. **199**. *Statuette of Lysikleides*. The statuette of Lysikleides, son of Epandrides, was dedicated in the same sanctuary; he is probably the figure represented holding a torch in each hand. It stands on its high ancient pedestal, charming us with the Classical balance in its movement, its style and its bright face. This delightful statue will have been produced in the workshop of Agorakritos by one of his pupils. 420-410 B.C.

No. **1783**. *Votive relief of Hermes and the Nymphs*. One of the greatest glories of the fifth century B.C. is the relief from the Kephisos at Phaleron. This has relief decoration on both its faces.

The inscription on the epistyle – "To Hermes and the Nymphs" – tells us to whom this relief was dedicated. The blue colour of the background is preserved in a number of places on the block, and the central *akroterion* of the pediment which crowned the relief (rather than the usual epistyle) will also have been coloured and gives holiness to this piece of art.

On the first panel the horses pulling the quadriga fill the central space. In the chariot are a couple – a young woman and a man who is looking lovingly towards her. In front is Hermes, the Leader of Brides, standing on a rise in the ground on which the feet of the horses are also treading, skilfully filling the space. Echelos and Basile, the names of the two figures, are inscribed on the epistyle. 420-410 B.C.

On the second panel the picture is more crowded; standing divinities, the horned god Kephisos in the centre, framed by Artemis and three Nymphs are represented. Found together with the likewise notable relief no. **2756**, an *ex-voto* of Xenokrateia.

No. 1783 Relief of Hermes and the Nymphs

No. **1500**. *The relief of the actors.* The highly praised relief of the actors dedicated to Dionysos, is of some significance for the history of the theatre. The god is stretched out on a bed, and calls to mind the Dionysos from the eastern pediment of the Parthenon. A young girl, most probably a symbolic figure, sits on the bed swinging her legs. A male dressed in the sleeved chiton worn by actors worships (venerates) the god, holding a mask in his left hand. The two standing figures behind him hold drums (*tympana*) and this suggests that the relief was dedicated after a performance of the *Bacchae* of Euripides. *Circa* 410 B.C.

No. **1419**. *Fragment from a relief decree.* Of the relief decrees set up by the Athenian state in order to publish enactments of varying content, only one fragment is exhibited in this room. The four standing figures of free citizens, dressed modestly in their himatia and advancing with their front legs thrust forward, give a picture of the Athenian state at its most creative period. Below are the remains of the inscription: "(name) was secretary". *Circa* 440 B.C.

No. **1571**. *Head of Hera from the Argive Heraion.* The architectural members from the temple of Hera take us to the Peloponnese where the Heraion stood on a high hill opposite Argos, facing the Argive plain spread out before it and the mountain massif. There are carved metopes and also pieces of the sima. Portrayed here is the serene head from a statue of Hera. Work of an Argeian (?) sculptor. *Circa* 420 B.C.

No. **1578**. *Torso of Aura (Breeze).* This full, strong torso of a Breeze (?) from the village of Chonika in the Argolid, reminds one, both by its subject and by the rendering of the folds, of an Attic *akroterion,* which will have served as its model. The Argeian sculptor, however, has given it a square shape and a Doric weightiness, so that it is difficult, though not impossible, to conceive of it as the *akroterion* of the temple of Hera, as has been suggested, unless it was an independent *ex-voto* in the goddess' sanctuary. *Circa* 420 B.C.

No. 199 Statuette of Lysikleides

61

No. 1500 The relief of the actors.
From Piraeus

No. **226**. *Votive stele from Mantineia.* Special significance has been given to the large engraved stele from Mantineia, the ancient city surrounded by mountains outside Tripolis, by the astute interpretation of a distinguished archaeologist. It was discovered in 1887, but it was only after 1936 that the name was given to the large-scale female figure, of which the head is unfortunately lost, who is wearing the Argive peplos and holding in her left hand a liver, undoubtedly for the purposes of divination. The theory was developed by H. Möbius, on the basis of the palm-tree, the tree of Apollo (only the lower part of the trunk survives), that this is none other than the famous Diotima, the prophetess of Plato's *Symposium*, whose native town was Mantineia, according to the Athenian philosopher. *Circa* 410 B.C.

TWO SMALL ROOMS WITH CLASSICAL WORKS

Before proceeding to the second room containing grave *stelai* of the fifth century B.C., we may turn aside to the right to the smaller rooms that open into the interior garden. In these a number of different fifth-century works are collected: statues, reliefs and copies of cult statues.

ROOM 19 (Small room to the left)

No **3572**. Two figures from one of the mose remarkable votive reliefs of its time. It is unusual in that Persephone is seated and Demeter standing – her name appears towards the rop of the anta beside her arm. Demeter's mature body fills the surface. Found in Athens, it will have been an *ex-voto* in the Eleunsinian sanctuary "of the Fields" beside the rives Ilissos. *Circa* 420 B.C.

No **1329**. The relief with the two very beautiful Nymphs, dedicated by Archandros – who is depicted on a smaller scale – as the inscription reveals, was found at the foot of the Acropolis in 1876. The upper part of Pan's bady projects beyond the mouth of a cave. *Circa* 410 B.C.

No **3569**. *Small head of Aphrodite.* The small head from Athens, has an Attic charm. It dates from the end of the fifth century B.C., and is a fragment of a statuette of Aphrodite, dedicated no doubt in an unknown sanctuary of the goddess in Attica. It is an imitation, rather than a direct copy, of a famous work by Kallimachos, which is known from a great number of large and small copies throughout the Roman world.

Roman copies of Classical works. The copies of Classical works commissioned by the Romans to adorn their palaces, villas, baths, palaestrae and even temples, conceal a different meaning. They were conscious, mechanical reproductions and thus lack the rhythmic movement and inspired expression of the divine persons, created with piety, imagination and artistry.

No **3949**. *Headless statue of a goddess.* The headless statue of a goddess from Athens, which dominates this room, is one, though not the best, of the Roman copies of the much praised statue of Neme-

No. 1571 Head of Hera from the
Argive Heraion

sis in the temple at Rhamnous, the work of Agorakritos, pupil of Pheidias.

ROOM 20 (Small room to the right)

The torso no. **1612** and the larger than life-size head no. **45** were found in the Olympieion in Athens in 1875 and belong to a renowned early work by Pheidias, the "Parnopios Apollo". (The best Roman copy is in Kassel). The head of the avenging god is imbued with a certain "intoxication" in its deep spirituality.

No. **3178.** In this colossal head of Athena, known as the "Pnyx Athena" after its find spot (1931), the coldness of the art of the Antonine period (second century A.D.) is repellent.The head was set in the body of a larger than life-size statue of the type known as the "Medici Athena", after the copy in the Louvre. The glacial effect of the polished surface is attributed to the attempted rendering of the ivory — the Pheidian original was chryselephantine.

No. **2182-85.** These fragments of relief plaques of lovely young girls dancing on tip-toe, the "Saltantes Lacaenae" of the Romans, echo creations by Kallimachos.

No **129.** *The "Varvakeion Athena".* The "Varvakeion Athena" is of interest only to the archaeologist. This statue reproduces on a smaller scale the chryselephantine Athena of Pheidias. It gives an idea not of its religious content, but only of its external appearance. Uninspired work of the second or third century A.D.

The interior garden was laid out as an open court during the reconstruction of the Museum after the war, and was intended as a resting place for the visitor sated with museum-viewing.
The visitor's attention is first attracted by a number of statues whose surface has been destroyed by salt. They were found in the depths of the sea off Antikythera in 1900, along with a large number of bronze objects from the Classical period. The marbles are copies or imitations of Classical works. The colossal Herakles in the central position in the court is a copy of a famous original by the great bronze sculptor Lysippos, called the "Farnese Herakles" after the best copy.

No **2773.** *Statue of a naked youth.* The statue of a naked youth on the point of adolescence has its surface preserved intact for the most part. The plinth has also survived. His weight is supported mainly on the right leg, which is bent, and he is holding his head upwards towards some opponent or possible fellow-competitor. His face calls to mind a young Satyr, though perhaps the sculptor merely wished to depict a foreign type. He may have been a wrestler or a dancer — we have no way of choosing between these two interpretations, both of which have been proposed. It is dated by its flat composition to the first century B.C.
The two large statues below the staircase, both of which are corroded, recall important models. There is no boubt that they depict heroes from the Epic cycle, and one of them is shown to be Odysseus by his hat.

No. 129 The "Varvakeion Athena"

No **3661.** *Stele of Theokles.* The stele of the young Theokles from Attica (the name is engraved on the epistyle) also has an attractive tenderness; the boy is playing with his dog, holding out a bird to it. It dates from the beginning of the fourth century B.C. or later.

Sarcophagi. Some deep-seated psychological change that we cannot now divine impelled the men of the second century A.D. onwards to bury their dead in sarcophagi bearing scenes carved in relief. Their compositions, and particularly those of the Attic sarcophagi, were to be used for the creation of new works by the artists of the Western Renaissance.

No. **4008.** *Sarcophagus from Athens.* The relief compositions are usually symbolic of the escape to the Elysian fields (Nereids and Tritons) or of the eternal "*intoxication*" (feasting of small children). The small Cupids carrying branches or crowns, or celebrating with Dionysos, embody a similar conception, but on the short sides of this sarcophagus, the sphinx is a sinister presence, suggesting death. The impressionistic rendering of the branch, and the use of the drill date the sacrophagus to the end of the second century A.D.*Circa* A.D. 200.

No. 723 The stele of Polyxene

ROOM 18 (Hegeso room)
(Second room of Classical grave reliefs)

No. **3624.** *Stele of Hegeso.* The stele of Hegeso stands in the centre of the second room containing grave reliefs. This is a much-sung monument, both to the Athenian desire to banish grief, and also to female beauty, and as such it corresponds in the area of Classical grave monuments to the statue of Phrasikleia (small room of Archaic sculptures). When it was dug from the earth of the Kerameikos, in 1870 it had a very profound effect, and Palamas dedicated a long poem of praise to it. At the time of its creation, about 410 B.C., after the inheritance of the school of Pheidias and when the effects of the disasters brought by the Peloponnesian War were being felt, the grave *stelai* began to take on a new size, and the pediment becomes its crown.

Hegeso wears the full dress of a bride in the relief, which stood on the family tomb. "Hegeso, daughter of Proxenos" is inscribed on the epistyle. The gold-painted piece of jewellery which Hegeso holds in her long slender fingers shone most effectively against the blue colour of the background, between the two figures who are turning their heads towards it. Hegeso has taken it from the *pyxis* which the servant girl is holding. The band above Hegeso's forehead will also have been golden. It is impossible to find words to praise the way in which her body is outlined beneath the light chiton, the beautiful lines of the legs, and even the carving of the chair. The leg of the standing girl also has a certain harmony. She is depicted as a slave girl wearing the barbarian sleeved chiton, which is unbelted and is lightly draped. The picture as a whole contains a silent grief and the mouth of Hegeso, half open, bitterly expresses her own sorrow. This, and this alone, is the only message of the scene. "You who pass by the monument, see how beautiful the young woman was who has

No. 3624 The famous funerary stele of Hegeso

passed away". Hegeso is the work, we may venture to suggest, of Kallimachos, and she remains unique and without parallel.

No. **717**. *Grave stele* from the Kerameikos, depicting a "banquet". Early fourth century B.C.

No. **726**. *Grave stele of a woman*. Immediately after the beginning of the fourth century B.C., the restrained grief is combined with a sense of agony and loneliness. In this stele from Piraeus, the dead woman is bowed in despair; she is not holding up a necklace, and not even gazing at the *pyxis*.

No. **723**. *Stele of Polyxene*. Polyxene in this stele, also from the Kerameikos cemetery, is even more sorrowful. The pediment is rather poor. She is sitting on a stool, with her head covered by her himation, and is stooping towards her little girl, who has her hands placed on her knees. Behind, at a secondary level, and almost not a part of the scene, is the standing figure of a servant girl. An epigram on the epistyle reads "here lies Polyxene, whose death caused great grief to her daughter, her husband, her mother and her father who sired her". *Circa* 400 B.C.

No. 752 The stele of Demokleides

No. **752**. *Stele of Demokleides*. The fate of the Greek sailor throughout the ages can be observed in the grave stele of Demokleides son of Demetrios, which is crowned with an epistyle. Its provenance is unknown. The prow of a trireme is outlined in front of the hoplite who is sitting on a rock and resting his head on his right hand in sorrow. A blue colouring will have indicated the bitter waves of the sea below it. The shield and the helmet show that he was a hoplite, who was possibly lost far from home, in which case the stele will have stood on his cenotaph.

No. **754**. *A funerary monument from the Polyandrion of Athens*. Only a few remains have been preserved of the monuments that adorned the Polyandrion, the state cemetery in the "very fair suburb" (Thucydides) of Athens. Here, near the centre of the Kerameikos, no. **754** was found in 1861; it is the crowning of a funerary monument, decorated with rich relief anthemia and acanthus leaves on volutes. Amongst the names of the Athenian cavalrymen who fell in the battles of Corinth and Koronea (394 B.C.), which are inscribed on the epistyle, is that of Dexileos. It has been observed that the rather conservative balance of the decoration of the epistyle is to be explained by the official nature of it.

ROOM 21 (The room of the Diadoumenos)

No. **15177**. *Horse and jockey of Artemision*. The problem whether the bronze horse and rider actually belong to the same composition remains unsolved. Only painstaking research on the part of art historians is likely to produce conclusive evidence. The horse is rendered in an attitude of extreme tension, both as regards the modelling of the head and the forward projection of both head and forelegs. The tre-

No. 15177 The bronze horse and "jockey" of Artemision; one of the most striking works of Greek art

mendous speed at which the horse is galloping causes the little chiton with numerous narrow folds worn by the jockey boy to be blown back. The boy's little face is constricted to the point of ugliness and his small lithe body contorted by the effort he is obliged to make. The work is a fascinating example of the human passion which artists of the peak period of the Hellenistic era succeeded in infusing into their most inspired works. Dated to about the mid-second century B.C.

No. **1826**. *Diadoumenos*. This room takes its name from the statue of the Diadoumenos which was found in Delos (1890) in a house of the late Hellenistic period. The statue is a copy of a famous bronze original by the Argean sculptor Polykleitos (about 420 B.C.), later than his "Canon", the Doryphoros (which is portrayed in the small grave relief from Argos next to it, no. **3153**). Carved at the beginning of the first century B.C., the Diadoumenos in the National Museum does not have the coldness of the mechanical copies made in the later Imperial period, and is not an arid work.

Nos. **1827**, **3622**. *Small Woman and Large Woman of Herculaneum type*. The female statue of the "Woman of Herculaneum" type supplies evidence for a slightly earlier period of Hellenistic Delos (end of the second century B.C.). The type is named after statues discovered in Herculaneum near Vesuvius. It is a copy of some famous original, possibly by Praxiteles, and the carving shows a richness and imagination in which the old tradition has not died out. Traces of colour are preserved on the hem of the himation, which does not cover the head, as in the corresponding statue, the "Large Woman from Herculaneum" (no. **3622**), itself a first-century A.D. copy of another original. It was found in 1926 in Athens, Stadiou Street, standing on an ancient tomb. Although the workmanship is uninspired, the great size of it, and the complicated folds of the garment show that the original came from the hand of a creative artist of broad imagination, probably a bronze sculptor from a centre in the North Peloponnese.

No. **720**. *Stele of Melite*. The figure of the dead woman in the large grave stele from Piraeus (discovered in 1836) has the solemnity of a statue. The name of Melite, wife of Spoudokrates of Phlyous, is inscribed on the epistyle of the shrine within which the figure is set. The original on which it was modelled (statue of a goddess?) is unknown. *Circa* 360 B.C.

No. **240**. *Hermes of Atalanti*. A funerary statue of a young man in the form of a god. He held a caduceus in his hand. Second century A.D.

No. **2308**. *Crowning member of a grave stele*. The heavy slab with the anthemion, from Athens, is a wonderful crowning member from one of the tall slender *stelai* of the fourth century B.C. It rises on volutes, and the out-turning leaves grow from bushy acanthus. *Circa* 350 B.C.

No 240 The Hermes of Atalanti

ROOM 22 (Epidauros room)

The most complete collection of architectural sculptures in the Museum is collected here. The sanctuary of Asklepios and the sculptures from his temple were uncovered by Panayotis Kavvadias in the years 1882-86, at the same time as the ancient Theatre and the richly decorated Tholos. According to the invaluable inscription discovered then, four sculptors worked on the decoration of the temple: Timotheos, Hektoridas, Theo... and a fourth whose name is not preserved.

Nos. **146a**, **4642**, **162**. *Sculptures from the east pediment of the temple of Asklepios.* The east pediment depicted the Sack of Troy. To it belonged the Trojan woman who is leaning back and raising an axe (or a large pestle?) in despair against her Greek foe (no. **146a**). Another sculpture from the same pediment is better preserved and has been successfully restored (no. **4642**): a woman is standing up to protect a little girl who has fled to her and is kneeling. The composition of the two figures has been developed in depth in a manner very advanced for the period (390-380 B.C.). The name of the sculptor Timotheos has been connected with the fine figure of a Victory (Nike, no. **162**) from the east pediment of the temple of Asklepios. The figure is winged, and the edge of her cloak is caught in the edge of the raised right wing.

No. **156**, **157**. *Akroteria of the temple of Asklepios.* We shall leave the figures and fragments of the west pediment (Amazonomachy) unexamined, for lack of space, and move on to the two akroteria of the temple – the two strange female figures riding horses, that have so far not been interpreted. As the animal emerges with its forelegs, it turns one's thoughts to the Ocean, from which the stars are rising. Possibly, then, the two figures represent gods of the stars, as has been suggested.

Architectural members from the Tholos. There are only a few charming fragments of the sima of the enigmatic Tholos, the restored parts of which enchant the visitor to the Museum at Epidauros. The carved crowning member is full of variety: there is a meander decoration, with a prolific rich curling plant above it, with leaves and acanthus flowers, and there are gargoyles at intervals in the shape of lions' heads with open mouths and wild deep-set eyes. The luxuriant foliage curls restlessly in deep shadow. The uncontrollable pathos of the second half of the fourth century B.C. finds its expression in the plants and other elements of the sima.

ROOM 23 (First room of grave stelai from the fourth century B.C.)

A new urban class was formed in Athens during the fourth century B.C. Weapon manufacturers, such as the wealthy Kephalos of Plato's *Republic*, shipowners and businessmen made their appearance alongside the old land-owning families. This fact alone would account for the richness of the memorials to the dead, even if at the same time there was not also in process that rejection of the city-state which had already commenced at the end of the fifth century B.C. There was also a decline in religious feeling. In place of the temples and cult statues – products of the city-state – the predominant monuments now are the large private tombstones,

No. 1826 The statue of the Diadoumenos. From Delos

No. 157 Akroterion from the temple of Asklepios at Epidauros

69

No. 751 The unusual stele of Alkias

No. 869 The stele of the Ilissos

which were produced by important sculptors and humble marble-carvers alike.

No. **817**. *Stele of a poetess*. Let us consider first a stele from outside Attica, one of the finest from the workshop at Thespiai. The young woman sitting on a stool shows direct rather than indirect descent from an Attic figure. She is leaning with her left arm on the pillow on the stool (the forearm has a vertical orientation) and is bending her head towards a naked boy, offering him some plaything (neither the boy nor the toy are completely preserved). The two cylindrical objects in the box above the stool have led to the suggestion that this is a picture of a poetess. The fact that her chiton is girded high necessitates a late date, in the second half of the fourth century B.C.

No. **751**. *Stele of Alkias*. The unusually small stele of Alkias of Phokis, from Corinth, departs from the Attic models. The way in which the hoplite Alkias strides triumphantly over the naked body of his opponent, and the chlamys hanging low behind him have an expressiveness that contrast with the restraint of Attic figures. End of the fifth century B.C.

No. **826**. *Stele from Salamis*. On the large stele from Salamis the poor low pediment does not match the simple grandeur of the two figures, standing face to face. The hand of the woman, which is extended as if in a farewell that precludes any hope of meeting again, lies precisely on the line of the central akroterion. About the middle of the fourth century B.C.

No. **870**. *Stele of the Farewell*. A special significance attaches to the "Stele of the Farewell", from Athens (1882), because of the rarity of the subject, the quality of the workmanship, and the dramatic departure. After the middle of the fourth century B.C.

No. **869**. *Stele of the Ilissos*. Nothing of substance can be added to all that has been written about the much praised "Stele of the Ilissos", except to note that the architectural members of the shrine in which it was discovered are missing. A pediment or an epistyle will have cast its shadow on the figures, reinforcing the deep emotion which they express. The small slave who is curled up on the stairway next to the feet of his master, half asleep in his childlike despair, and the hunting dog sniffing the ground are undoubtedly scenes from life, added by a great artist of the third quarter of the fourth century B.C. It is possible that the creator of the monument was Skopas.

Nos. **2583, 774**. *Sepulchral Sirens*. The sphinxes above the Archaic *stelai*, heavy at first but smiling and slender in the second half of the sixth century B.C. are replaced in the fourth century by sepulchral Sirens. They have been described as "Muses of the afterworld" because they sing in sorrow and consolation above the graves. Some of them lament, tearing the curls of their hair (no. **2583**), and others hold a lyre. No. **774**, discovered in the Kerameikos in 1863, sings a lament, holding a primitive lyre (of tortoise-shell). She is framed by her open wings, and her sorrowing face is well forward.

ROOM 24 (Second room of grave monuments of the fourth century B.C.)

Nos. **823-824**. *Scythian archers*. The grave monuments in this room continue to be varied, though the main shape is that of the small shrine. The full length statues of a young seated servant girl, no. **825**, and two Scythian archers, nos. **823-824**, stood out in front of two small shrines, which have not been preserved. The latter, who were probably guarding the tomb of an Athenian official of this period, were discovered in the Kerameikos in 1836. Second half of the fourth century B.C.

No. **825**. *Statue of a servant girl*. The full length servant girl is sitting on a rock in a mournful pose, and there will have been a similar statue at the other corner of the monument. It will have stood above a grave outside the north wall of the city (it was discovered in Stadiou Street in 1887). Middle of the fourth century B.C.

Apart from the large and small shrines, an idea of the rich picture presented by the Athenian and Attic cemeteries in their verdant situations in the fourth century B.C. is given by the smaller *stelai*, the fragments of funerary *loutrophoroi*, dogs from the tombs of huntsmen, and Sirens.

No. 3716 The "Bright-shining monument". Stele of a young woman

No. **737**. *Grave monument of the famiy of Prokleides*. The large shrine of Prokles and Prokleides was more fortunate than other monuments of this period which lost their frames. The names of the people portrayed are inscribed on the epistyle below the pediment. The composition depicts three figures; the father is seated on the extreme left, and is receiving his son, now a mature man and a warrior, while between them, in the background, the mother has covered her head with her himation. Above is the name, Prokles, son of Prokleides from Aegile, and also that of the woman, Archippe, daughter of Meikiades from Aegile. The monument was found in the Kerameikos in 1861, and is dated to 330-320 B.C.

No. **3716**. *The "bright shining monument"* The stele next to it is also without its architectural surroundings; it was described by Chr. Karouzos, in the publication of it which was his archaeological swan-song, as the "bright shining monument". The seated god-like female figure who fills the large central part of the block, is lifting the edge of her himation with her right hand. The figure has a breadth unusual in grave stele. This wonderful monument attests the "high" imagination and the hand of an excellent sculptor of about 370 B.C.

No. **2574**. *Grave monument of the family of Alexos from Sounion*. The large monument of Alexos was found in the district of Aghios Rendis outside Athens, and it was during the post-war years that it was first set up together with its splendid cornice, which until then had lain forgotten in one of the Museum's store-rooms. We must accept that the composition had four figures because of the size of the crowning member, and in particular the names inscribed above on the epistyle. Only Alexos, the father, is preserved, standing on the left. His wife, Philoumene, will have been seated in front of him to the right, receiving his son, Stratokles, standing. The name Phanostrate,

No. 3619 Crowning device from a large funerary monument

carved on the epistyle without patronymic, refers to the servant girl who will have stood in the background between the two last figures, in low relief. The names, in order, are: *Alexos, son of Stratokles, from Sounion. Philoumene, daughter of Philoxenos, from Marathon. Phanostrate,* (and finally) *Stratokles, son of Alexos, from Sounion. Circa 320 B.C.*

No. **3619**. *Large grave monument*. The inventive imagination of the workshops producing grave monuments in Athens during the fourth century B.C. can be seen in the large monument from Athens in the centre of the room. There is a marble fluted cauldron, with the upright necks and heads of griffins at intervals – all reminiscent of the earlier bronze *lebetes*. *Circa* 340 B.C.

No. **819**. *Grave stele of a young mother*. A number of *stelai* show a simple humanity without being artistically ambitious. The theme of the lost young mother particularly touched men's hearts, it seems; we can still feel a silent sympathy in the portrayal of the young grieving mother seated on a rich throne (to show that she has been heroised). The child, with pointed hat, is in the arms of a servant girl, and the whole picture is an idealised, other-worldly composition of the atmosphere in the women's quarters. This stele, which originally had the form of a small shrine, was found in Piraeus. Middle of the fourth century B.C.

ROOM 25-27 (Small rooms with reliefs from decrees and dedications)

The reliefs carved on decrees constitute one of the most eloquent pieces of evidence for the public activity of the Athenian democracy, and also for the role played in it by art. Figures are carved in relief above the decrees engraved on the lower part of the stele, which were prompted by various motives:
1) Decrees containing treaties with other cities.
2) Honorific decrees, or awards of *proxenia* to foreigners who have conferred some benefit, or who it is hoped will confer some benefit, on the Athenian democracy.
3) The accounts of the state treasurers of the money dedicated to the gods – mainly to Athena. (In the relief no. **1479**, Athena is holding out her hand to a bearded figure, the Athenian People.)
A firm chronology for the monuments is supplied by the names of the officials referred to in the inscriptions.

ROOM 25

No. **1467**. *Relief decree from Attica*. A relief containing a long decree commemorating the treaty between Athens and Corcyra (374/3 B.C.) is adorned with the figure of Athena, representing the Athenian state. Corcyra is in the centre, full-face, with the Athenian People seated on the left.

No. **1471**. *Relief decree*. The domination of the space by the artist, following in the wake of paintings from the second half of the fourth century B.C., can be seen in a relief plaque on the upper part of a tall

No. 1467 Relief from an Attic stele with a decree

heavy stele of 347/6 B.C. (archonship of Themistokles). The decree is in honour of the three sons of Leukon, king of the Cimmerian Bosporos. It stood in ancient times in the harbour of Piraeus.

Nos. **2011-2012, 1445**. *Reliefs of Nymphs*. The majority of the reliefs dedicated to the Nymphs, in the shape of a cave, were discovered in the cave on Parnas, and at Vari in Attica, where they were dedications in the cave of Nympholeptos. Hermes is watching the dance of the Nymphs and Pan appears above, holding his pipe (nos. **2011-2012**, from Vari). In a more humble relief from Eleusis (no. **1445**), the figure watching the dance in front of the altar is Pan, not Hermes, and below is the bust of the river Acheloos. Fourth century B.C.

No. 3942 Many-figured votive relief. From Leivadia

Boeotian reliefs. The few Boeotian reliefs in this room appear foreign amongst all the Attic works; they furnish valuable evidence, however, for those places which, though bordering on Attica, remained attached to the spirits of the earth and continued to believe in their power.

No. **1861**. *Heavy relief block*. The figures in the heavy relief block, discovered in Thebes in 1896, remain unexplained; it was probably dedicated to dead men worshipped as heroes. It must have been very difficult to work the hard, local Thespian stone. The entire picture with its frontal figures displays a provincial, somewhat gauche stiffness. Late fifth century B.C.

No. **3942**. *Many-figured relief*. The small narrow relief from Leivadia (found in 1935) with its many figures, is unique. Otto Walter, who interpeted the work, divined that amongst the twelve large and four small figures are depicted Trophonios, bearded, with two snakes behind him, the Kouretes, the Dioskouroi, and other gods. The oracle of Chthonian Trophonios was at Leivadia. The figure with its head covered by a skin represents initiation into the mysteries. Probably from the third century B.C.

No. **693**. *Statuette of a girl*. Returning to Attic works, we may examine the charming statuettes from the beginning of the third century B.C. which depict young girls. These are not funerary, as some others like them, but votive. They were discovered in the Ilissos, and they must have been dedicated by the parents of the children to the goddesses of childbirth, the Eileithyes, who were worshipped in the shrine of Agra on the nearby hill.

An attempt has been made in the statuette of the young girl to portray the fluttering garments blowing in the wind. 300-290 B.C..

No. **1403**. *Part of a votive relief in the form of a shrine*. When they wished to portray gods and goddesses in the reliefs, the marble-carvers naturally did not invent new types. Many of the figures are reminiscent of cult statues, which they did not copy faithfully, as others did some centuries later, but with a certain freedom, either because they were presented with different figures, or because they believed in the existence of the gods they were depicting in the statues and wanted to make them come alive. The sculptor of the large relief from Piraeus followed his model most faithfully. Even though suppliants were portrayed in the right-hand part of the monument, which is

No. 1403 Fragment of a votive relief in the form of a small shrine

No. 1332 Relief of Athenian doctors. From the Asklepieion

not preserved, the marble-worker was obliged by the fact that he was following a statue of Kore (Persephone) to depict the goddess full-face. Just after 420 B.C.

No. **3917**. *Votive relief in the form of a shrine*. Cult statues of the Delian triad set up in Athens are portrayed *en face*, in a relief in the form of a shrine (of unknown provenance). Leto is in the middle, with her two children, Apollo and Artemis; they all have the sacred lack of movement of Classical models, emphasised by the shadows that result from their having been set in depth below the epistyle. Second half of the fourth century B.C.

Reliefs from the Asklepieion in Athens. In 420/19 B.C. Asklepios, the god of Epidauros, "arrived" in Athens from Zea, the harbour in Piraeus, through the intervention of a private individual. Sophocles received him in his home and in 413/2 the god was established in his own sanctuary, the Asklepieion, below the southern slopes of the Acropolis, which was uncovered by the excavations of the Archaeological Society in 1877. In almost all the reliefs the faces of the figures of the god and his family have disappeared as a result of the relentless battering they received at the hands of Christian fanatics, who found them still standing in late antiquity (the worship of the healer-god survived longer than that of all the other Olympians). These reliefs are of the usual type – the shrine with an epistyle – and most of them reflect painted wooden plaques hung as dedications in the sanctuary of the god.

He is depicted upright, in the form of his statue, which was erected in the last quarter of the fifth century B.C., and next to him, ready to receive the worshippers, are his wife, Epione, Hygeia, and his sons the Asklepiades (though they are not always depicted). The worshippers, men, women and children, are smaller than the gods; the servant girl carries a basket on her head holding the offerings, the "sacrificial cakes" that will be laid on the altar. A small slave sometimes leads the lamb for the sacrifice. Most of them are the works of unambitious marble-carvers, and are relevant rather to the field of religion than to that of art, but they are attractive above all for their simple narrative, and the humane expression of Asklepios, as he stoops to the suppliants who are beseeching his aid, or coming to express their gratitude for his healing powers with their dedication.

No. **1338**. *Cornice*. The earliest reliefs from the Asklepieion are crowned with a simple horizontal cornice. The earliest relief of all will have been dedicated in the years immediately following the founding of the temple; it is also the best in quality. The relief, Classical in the best sense of the word, will have been dedicated about 410-400 B.C., and is the work of a good sculptor.

No. **1333**. *Relief of Hygeia*. As the fourth century B.C. advances, the reliefs have more figures, as worshippers are added, and the shrine takes on a more tectonic form. The figure in this relief reflects a fourth-century B.C. statue of Hygeia.

No. **1332**. *Relief of Athenian doctors*. The names engraved in a crown below the figures of the six worshippers in this relief, inform us that they were Athenian physicians, three of them sons of famous

No. 2565 Votive relief

doctors. They dedicated the relief to Asklepios and the two Eleusinian deities. Second half of the fourth century B.C.

No. **1841**. *Relief with a scene of enkoimesis.* A scene of the *enkoimesis* (sleeping in the temple) in the Asklepieion in Athens is depicted in this relief. These scenes are humorously bought to life by Aristophanes in the *Ploutos*, and this relief cannot, therefore, be later than that work, and is thus one of the earliest of its type. Asklepios is sitting beside the man lying on the bed and rubbing the sick man's arm. The large standing male figure will be one of the Asklepiades, Podaleirios or Machaon. The inscription on the epistyle reads: "During the priesthood of Diophanes, son of Apollonios". End of the fifth century B.C.

No. **2565**. *Votive relief.* The old interpretation by Chr. Tsountas of the tall narrow relief with the snake, the sandal and the worshipper has not been surpassed. It must have been dedicated to the "hero in the sandal", who was worshipped somewhere near the site where this unique relief was found in 1904, not far from the theatre of Dionysos. "Silon dedicated (me)" runs the incription below the sandal, and he is portrayed in the relief figure. *Circa* 360 B.C.

No. 3369 Votive relief from the Amphiareion at Oropos

ROOM 26

No. **3369**. *Votive relief, dedication to Amphiaraos from Archinos.* Another doctor hero (he was never worshipped as a god) was the seer Amphiaraos, who was swallowed up by the earth as he was returning from the expedition against Thebes. A votive relief was found in his shrine near Oropos, with a very complete picture of an *enkoimesis*, connected with two other scenes depicting chronologically successive events. In the foreground the young man is standing and receiving treatment on his shoulder from a tall man, possibly a priest. Behind, on a second plane, an erect snake is licking the shoulder of the young man who is asleep on the bed. Next follows the scene of the dedication of the relief on a base by the young man himself, now healed. His name can be read below the figures: "Archinos dedicated (me) to Amphiaraos". First half of the fourth century B.C.

No. **1384**. *Fragment of a relief.* The fragment of another relief, coming not from the Asklepieion at Athens but from the Amphiareion at Rhamnous, is of the type well known from the Athenian shrine. Luckily the faces of the dedicators have been preserved on the right (the left part, on which the god was portrayed, is missing). *Circa* 350 B.C.

ROOM 28 (Grave monuments of the fourth century B.C.)

No. **738**. *Grave shrine of Aristonautes.* Another architecturally rich monument discovered in recent years, not far from Aghios Rendis, will, like the large monuments we have already seen, have probably provoked protest from the people who were seeking equality. It was exploited for demagogic purposes by the Macedonian governor De-

No. 4496 Left jamb of a funerary shrine

No. 738 The funerary stele of Aristonautes
No. 4464 Large funerary monument from Kolonos

metrios of Phaleron, a gifted, ingenious pupil of Aristotle. In Athens, however, he inflicted a blow on art with a law of 317 B.C. forbidding the erection of grave monuments. In the *stelai* immediately preceding this law, the isolation of the figure of the dead man has advanced considerably and is carved in much deeper relief, so that the body stands out from the surfaace of the monument almost in the round. The figures now move within the space, in a shady atmosphere created by their architectural surroundings, and especially by the pediment.

Aristonautes is depicted alone in one of these splendid shrines (discovered in the Kerameikos in 1864). The face, with its deeply shadowed eyes and burning emotion, puts the stele on the same level as that from the Ilissos. A mark of the wisdom of its creator is the way in which he has placed an epistyle between the tall helmet and the pediment. On this is carved in the clear script of the fourth century B.C.: "Aristonautes, son of Archenautes from Halieis".

No. **1283**. *Door-post decoration of a funerary shrine.* A number of the shrines must have had relief decoration on the sides too. Here the faithful servants of the family are depicted, as in this stele, with the young girl wearing the barbarian sleeved chiton, and the "net" holding her hair in place. She is portrayed full-face, with her hands clasped low, but the provincial sculptor has succeeded in emphasising a childlike carefree expression in her face. It was discovered at Rhamnous, and is dated to 320-310 B.C.

No. **4496**. *Left door-post of a funerary shrine.* There is a similar figure carved in low relief on the side of a shrine now lost but which was undoubtedly of exceptional workmanship (from Attica). The barbarian woman is depicted here full of silent sorrow, her hair cut short in grief, and she is raising the fingers of her left hand towards her left cheek and in front of the eye. *Circa* 310 B.C.

No. **4464**. *The monument with the horse.* . The "monument with the horse", was a dazzlingly unexpected discovery of the post-war years. It was found in Athens in 1948, near to Kolonos, and the dating of it has given rise to opposing views. It consists of two blocks only, but at least one more is missing, and possibly the whole crowning member. On the right a young Ethiopian groom is trying to control a large horse, offering it some food which is not clearly defined. The head of the horse is inspired, projecting as it does away from the block, while the body remains attached to it. Above the horse's back there are traces of a painted helmet (belonging to the horseman, who is not portrayed). The intense, spasmodic movement of the groom, the whip in one hand, the extended legs, the anxious face opposite the animal's head, the contrast between the head of the dead skin of the panther and the open eyes of the horse, and the whole muscular body of the latter — all these reveal the work of a bold artist fired with the Greek genius. The whole shape of the monument and the style of the carving in deep relief derive from the tradition of the last Attic *stelai* before the law of 317. B.C. We may place him during the first half of the third century B.C., when grave monuments were no longer being erected in Attic cemeteries.

No. 3602 Head of the goddess Hygeia. From Tegea

No. 13396 The Youth of Antikythera

No. 231 Statue of the goddess
Themis. From Rhamnous

No. 6439 The famous bronze head
of a boxer. From Olympia

ROOM 28 (Room of the youth from Antikythera)

No. **13396**. *The Youth from Antikythera*. The dominating central position in this room is occupied by the bronze statue of the youth, which is one of the few large-scale ancient bronzes to have survived. It was discovered in many pieces in 1900 by divers, in the depths of the sea off Antikythera, along with a large number of marble statues and a lesser number of bronze statuettes. Many interpretations of the figure have been put forward: Perseus holding the Medusa's head (which is impossible), Paris holding the apple, and an athlete holding a ball – the last for want of a better interpretation. It has the form of a Classical statue, with that rhythm in the body that the Greeks were the only people of the ancient world to study and achieve successfully. Newer elements from the fourth century are the turning of the head towards the relaxed right leg, which is drawn back so that only the toes touch the ground. In this way the figure is successfully opened up towards the front. The harmony of the left arm, hanging free, defies description. It is balanced by the looseness of the right leg, while the left is tensed, to match the right arm. The work is without doubt an original, and there can be no question of its being a recasting in the Roman period. This is clear from, amongst other things, the curls of the hair, which fall rich, thick and wavy from the parting on the relatively narrow forehead. Their appearance presupposes that they were worked "cold" and engraved and shaped after the "hot" casting of the metal around the core. The Peloponnesian artist, one of the best of his age, has based himself on the "Canon" of Polykleitos of a century earlier, and has given the pose a lightness worthy of Lysippos. The strong chest derives from the Polykleitian heritage, while the formation of the anatomy of the abdomen, and the wonderful way in which the back is marked out, are the personal contribution of the sculptor. *Circa* 340 B.C.

No. **3602**. *Head of the goddess Hygeia*. As well as the sculptures from the temple of Asklepios at Epidauros, there are some few important remains from the temple of Athena Alea near Tegea. The ruins of it still come as a surprise in the green village in Arkadia. It was built after 395 B.C. when the earlier temple was destroyed by fire. The architect and sculptor was Skopas. The few remaining warriors' heads have an expression of burning emotion; they have been divided between the Tegea Museum and the National Museum. In contrast the head of the goddess Hygeia, turned to the left, has a divine sweetness. It was probably from her cult statue and is not weighed down by thick hair. The great sculptor (if the statue is indeed the work of Skopas) envisaged the daughter of the healing god as assuager of human pain. The surface of the face has vanished as a result of corrosion. *Circa* 360 B.C.

No. **6439**. *Bronze head of a boxer*. Found at Olympia in 1880, the head is almost god-like in the treatment of the hair and thick beard, worked "cold" after casting. The olive wreath indicates a victor in the games and the snub nose and cauliflower ears suggest a boxer. The statue to which the head belonged, a work of Silanion, portrayed the boxer Satyros. It will have been erected in the Altis about 330 B.C.

No. **182**. *Head of a goddess*. The large female head, discovered in the theatre of Dionysos in Athens, helps us to imagine what it would have looked like in antiquity. From the broad band encircling the head (the Dionysiac *mitra*), Franz Studniczka, a distinguished archaeologist, has concluded that it belonged to a statue of Ariadne resting on Naxos, where Theseus abandoned her after bringing her with him from Crete. Second half of the fourth century B.C.

No. 262. *Statue of the "armed Aphrodite"*. The subject of the "armed Aphrodite" in a statue of the goddess discovered at Epidauros in 1886, remains problematical. The work has the Classical chiastic composition in its pose, and the head is turned towards the leg bearing the weight. The beautiful carving, especially of the diaphanous chiton, could date the work as early as the Classical period. However, the harsh rendering of the curls, and particularly the lack of any attempt to give a plastic effect to the rear view, reveal that it is the work of a more recent copyist, probably schooled in an Athenian workshop of the first century A.D.

No. **1733**. *The "base of Bryaxis"*. If the treatise by Polemon of Troy (second century A.D.) had survived, in which he gives a description of the dedications to Dionysos set up in the Street of the Tripods ("Περί των εν Αθήνησι τριπόδων"), we would be in a position to conjure up some picture of how this street would have looked, circling, as it did, the Acropolis on its south-west fringe. A good idea of the captivating beauty of these dedications in the fourth century B.C. is given by the monument of Lysikrates, although its crown, the undoubtedly exceedingly beautiful tripod, is now missing. The two tripods whose bases are exhibited in this room will have been humbler dedications. The first of them, no. **1733**, is square and was discovered in 1891. The name of the artist is inscribed on it: "Bryaxis made (me)". Middle of the fourth century B.C.

No. **1463**. *Triangular bronze base of a tripod*. The base of the other tripod is triangular. It was found in 1853 in Tripodon Street, and is decorated on all three sides with relief figures standing on a horizontal projection. Second half of the fourth century B.C.

ROOM 29 (The Themis room)

No. **231**. *Statue of Themis*. This room takes its name from the large statue of the goddess discovered in 1890 at Rhamnous, Attica. It has survived together with its base, where the inscription of the artist, Chairestratos of Rhamnous, is incised, along with the name of the dedicator Megakles, also of Rhamnous. When we consider that much earlier Agorakritos, a pupil of Pheidias, had produced the statue of Nemesis, who was worshipped in this place along with Themis, the provincial nature of the statue of Themis becomes clear, and we may suspect that religion declined during the third century B.C. on this distant, unforgettable hill in Attica. Third century B.C.

No. **247**. *Statue of a Gaul*. The body of the conquered Gaul from Delos, next to the statue of Themis, comes from a Hellenistic centre. The work gains a sense of explosive drama from the addition by J. Marcadé of a head which was in the Museum on Delos. End of the third century B.C.

No. 1737 Part of the "Sacred garment" of the goddesses of Lykosoura

No. 232 Statue of the priestess Aristonoe. From Rhamnous

No. 2772 Statuette of a boy with a duck. From Lilaia

Discoveries from the Sanctuary of Lykosoura

The ancient cults, however, remained alive in distant parts of Mainland Greece. The countryside around Lykosoura in Arkadia is "Arkadian" in the sense that became attached to the word in more recent periods; one's mind is overwhelmed as one stands in that deserted spot where Pan, with his goat's feet and his pipes, still lies in wait. The main goddess worshipped in the shrine, whose ruins were uncovered in 1889, was Despoina, a very ancient goddess of vegetation, the earth, life and death. Later she was called the daughter of Demeter and of Poseidon Hippios, who himself remained there as a god of the underworld.

Pausanias states explicitly that the statues of the temple were the work of Damophon of Messene, a sculptor who specialised in the art of acrolithic statues and in the repair of old chryselephantine ones. We know that he was active in the second century B.C. It is amazing that at the beginning of this century, K. Kourouniotis succeeded in bringing the three large heads to the National Museum, though the colossal bodies remained in the Lykosoura Museum. They must be imagined as they stood there in that other-worldly, verdant spot, together with the heads of the National Museum. The description of Pausanias is supplemented by the picture on an Arkadian coin, showing the two goddesses, Despoina and Demeter, seated in the middle and framed by the standing figures of the Titan Anytos and Artemis. Despite the corrosion of the surface, they may be dated the second century B.C.

Nos. **1736**, **1734**, **1737**. *Heads of Anytos, Demeter and Despoina.* The head of Anytos (no. **1736**) has a fluid rendering of the hair and beard, and equally fluid carving, which has succeeded in producing soft, shadowed even surfaces. There is a similar delicacy in the rendering of the hair on the head of Demeter (no **1734**). The temperament of a Helladic sculptor, who was not entirely devoid of the influence of Classicism, can be detected in the expressions of the human faces which, compared with Classical statues, are somewhat vacant. The "holy garment" of Despoina, however, has a purely Hellenistic charm (no. **1737**) (her head was not found), and marks a successful attempt to translate to marble from another material.

Nos. **2171**, **2175**. *Female Tritons.* Some of the female Tritons, decorating the throne, have a lithe beauty. One of them, no. **2171**, carries the mystic basket on her head. As for the female Triton no. **2175**, which is cold with a stiff body and unexpressive carving, there can be no doubt that it comes from a repair of the monument in the second century A.D., during the reign of Hadrian.

ROOM 30 (Hellenistic sculpture room)

This room is devoted to the Hellenistic period, and it would be poor enough without the three bronze portrait heads. This phenomenon is easily understood when one thinks of the destruction, pillaging of cities and plundering of works of art in the Greek world by the Romans from the second century B.C. Aemilius Paullus alone, who defeated Perseus, brought with him so many works of art that 250 ox-carts were needed to carry them in his triumpal procession, in which the

Macedonian king and his children were forced to march as prisoners of war; we are far from the Greek aversion for such "triumphs", which incurred the wrath of the gods. The "Greek spoils, the plunder of Corinth", amazed the Italian youth in the well known poem of Kavafy, when they were unloaded on the shore. On that occasion, in 146 B.C., the plunderers even dug up tombs to find treasures. The vases robbed from the tombs were known as "Necrocorinthia" in Rome, and their fine technique bewildered the conquerors.

No. **2772**. *Statuette of a naked boy*. He leans against a colonnette and clutches a duck in his left hand. Found near Lilaia at the foot of Mount Parnassus. Third century B.C.

No. **13400**. *The philosopher of Antikythera*. The striking head of a philosopher, retrieved from the depths of the sea off Antikythera, combines personal characteristics with a formal ideal. The feet which perhaps belong to it (nos. **15091, 15114**), with sandals from this period, show that he was not a bare-footed Cynic philosopher, but he nonetheless stood heavily on both soles, as philosophers are usually portrayed. It is a living picture of an observant, sceptic philosopher of the Hellenistic period, from the hand of some unknown sculptor. It has been suggested that it may be a portrait, showing a psychological competence unknown in earlier statues, of Bion the Borysthenite, a third-century B.C. philosopher who left his mark on the age with his satyrical "diatribes". The fluid composition of the Hellenistic figure (hair almost uncombed, cheeks, wrinkles on the forehead etc.) is confirmed by comparison with the balanced, closed classical form of the boxer's head.

No. **232**. *Statue of Aristinoe*, priestess of Nemesis. Set up by her son, Hierakles, in the sanctuary at Rhamnous This is a provincial work of the Late Hellenistic period.

No. **234**. *Colossal bust of Athena*. No. **233**: *Torso of a Nike*. The colossal bust of Athena was discovered in 1837 in the outer Kerameikos, along with the torso of Nike, and with fragments of the base – all of them parts of a dedication produced by the Athenian sculptor Euboulides in the second century (about 130 B.C.). The complete statue of Athena will have been a repetition, though not a mechanical one, of an archetype possibly by Kresilas (the type is known as Athena Veletri after the best copy).

In Athens, which was deserted in the second century B.C. and lived with the memories of its glorious name – the "great name of Athens" as the general Nikias so tragically called it to his fellow soldiers in the Sicilian disaster – the art of the portrait statue flourished in the second and first centuries B.C. The figures of the philosophers and the many foreigners who studied in Athens were the source of inspiration for the statue makers.

No. **3266**. *Head of a poet (?)*. The statue of the poet, probably seated, of which only the head has survived, will have stood in the Stoa of Attalos. If it is correctly dated to *circa* 150 B.C., it is strange that it escaped the almost total plundering of Athens by the monster Sulla (86 B.C.). At this date only philosophers insisted in wearing a beard; others, and especially the poets, had adopted the Macedo-

No. 13400 The bronze head of a philosopher. From the sea bed off Antikythera

No. 351 Portrait head of a foreign priest

nian custom of shaving the face. A rare stroke of luck has preserved the nose of the poet, and the facial expression is thus complete. The carving of the skin is executed with loving care, in contrast with the thick hair. The face has an expression of unforgettable melancholy, the tragic sense of isolation that was a reflection of the collapse of the idea of the city-state.

No. **351**. *Portrait head of a foreign priest*. In the Late Hellenistic period, there must have been study of the racial characteristics of the foreigners who found work in Athens – of the priests who served the large numbers of foreign deities from the East that were introduced in increasing numbers into the Olympic Pantheon. The portrait head of a beardless priest (from Athens), is one of the best mainland works of this period. The sculptor has depicted the racial element with ruthless realism. We can recognise that he was a Thracian from the pronounced zygomatic bones and the small expressionless eyes. The crown of leaves has been rendered in marble with the utmost skill, as have the curls around the temples and the throat and, above all, the dry skin of the mature blond northerner. The statue of the foreign priest will have been erected in the first half of the first century B.C.

Nos. **1485-1486**. *Votive stelai*. The two unusual votive *stelai*, known from two old sketches by the famous painter Gyzis (1865), transport us to the distant region of Nikaia in Bithynia. The richer of the two is no. **1485**, which has one main relief, with others below it in two bands, all carved in low relief. An inscription on seven columns below it informs us that men and women members of a guild bestowed a crown on the priestess of Apollo and Cybele (119 B.C.). The other votive stele from Nikaia, no. **1486**, is more simple. Here also, the dominating figure in the hollow plaque is a goddess; she is slender wears the chiton and himation, and is holding a sceptre in her left hand and a phiale in the right, with which she is pouring a libation over an altar. Below there is a six-line inscription.

No. **235**. *Statue of Poseidon*. The room is dominated by the statue of Poseidon, which stood in his temple on the distant island of Melos. The posture shows a slight decline from the dynamic centrifugal emphasis of earlier works from the first half of the second century B.C. The dolphin is an ingenious device, forming a living support beside the right leg. The vacant expression is typical of the age, and the whole portrayal, probably by a good, provincial Cycladic sculptor, was influencedd by statues of gods or leaders that stood in the great centres of Asia Minor. *Circa* 130 B.C.

No. **14612**. *Bronze head of a man*. Bronze head of a man found in the palaestra at Delos in 1912. It probably formed part of a statue of a standing male figure, wearing a himation. The head is turned to the left, but the man's glance, directed slightly upwards, as though he were gazing into space, reflects an interior world full of anxiety and uncertainty. The work is a superb rendering of a man of the early first century B.C. who is perhaps meditating nostalgically on the turbulent years of the Hellenistic era, yet without faith or hope in a world filled

No. 14612 Excellent bronze male head. From Delos

No. 235 The large, marble statue of Poseidon, discovered on Melos

with doubts. The work is one of the finest sculptured portraits of the Late Hellenistic period. Early first century B.C.

No. **1156**. *Grave stele of a woman*. The prolific survival of the grave *stelai* in the Cyclades and the Ionian cities of Asia Minor is attested by a great number of examples. Only a faint idea of this is given by the small number of Hellenistic *stelai* in this room. A stele from Rheneia is a distinctive work of art. The dead woman is named below it: "Lampron of Stymphalos, good wife of Sarapion, greetings". The young woman, Lampron, is represented heroised in the from of a known statue from Delos. A maid-servant on the left is holding the *pyxis* from the women's quarters, and a fan. We shall never know how the young Peloponnesian woman, wife of an Egyptian (merchant on Delos?) came to be buried in the cemetery of Rheneia; however, the grief in her tender face is compelling, as is the whole picture, so lovingly chiselled by the sculptor. *Circa* 120 B.C.

No. 260 Plaque with a relief of a dancing girl. From the theatre of Dionysos

Nos. **3556**, **429**. *Portraits of Hellenistic princes*. One of the two portraits of Hellenistic princes (with the diadem around the head), no. **3556**, was found in 1887 on the western slopes of the Acropolis, and the other, no. **429** (second century B.C.) on Delos. The latter is larger than life and is corroded by salt, but is the finer, more impassioned work. The feeling of the period of the Epigoni is expressed by the head being turned upward – an inheritance from the type of the head of Alexander the Great. The statue may depict Mithridates Eupator, ruler of Pontus. The Hellenistic passion in the head no. **3556** from Athens is mingled with a classical calm. The diadem shows that he was a prince, and the fleshy hooked nose and small eyes that he was from the East. A sensitive sculptor of about 120 B.C. produced this portrait of Ariarathes V of Cappadocia, the philhellene king who studied in Athens. The statue may have stood in the Stoa of Attalos.

Nos. **221-222**. *Relief frieze from Thermopylai*. A poetical development in the symbolism surrounding death is revealed in the small relief frieze discovered near Thermopylai. It shows Tritons, male and female, and Cupids riding on sea animals. *Circa* 70 B.C.

No. **3377**. *Head of Zeus*. Colossal cult statues were still set up in the sanctuaries of the Peloponnese in the second century B.C. The head of Zeus is an exceptional piece of plastic art and expresses well the Hellenistic ideal; it was undoubtedly set on a seated acrolithic statue which was one of the finest of its period. When it was discovered at Aigeira in Achaea in 1916, it was immediately recognised as belonging to the masterpiece of the sculptor Eukleides, seen by Pausanias in the second century A.D. The left arm of the statue has survived, and a finger from the right hand (nos. **3481**, **3481a**).

Nos. **259-260**. *Two plaques with dancing girls in relief*. The two plaques with the relief carvings of dancing girls were found in the theatre of Dionysos in 1862. The way the plaques are hollowed on their faces shows that, along with a third (no. **2667**, next to them), they formed the base of a bronze tripod dedicated to the god. The

No. 3335 Marble group of Aphrodite and Pan. From Delos

No. 4465 Relief of Nymphs. From Pentele

dancing girl, covered to the top of her head by the himation, is a copy of some beautiful model from the second half of the fourth century B.C. Her movement and whole appearance is as light as air. End of the first century B.C.

No. **3335**. *Group including Aphrodite and Pan*. Found at Delos. Pan, goat-footed, is trying to embrace the naked goddess who has removed her left sandal with which she teasingly threatens to strike him. A little Eros flies above the goddess' shoulder and seizes hold of one of Pan's horns. A show of more warmth of feeling would have provided charm to a work which is, in reality, little more than a purely pictorial representation devoid of inspiration. *Circa* 100 B.C.

ROOM 31 (Temporarily closed)

Rooms 31-33 are temporarily closed. In the future reorganisation of the Museum sculptures will be exhibited here. The Stathatos Collection and gold jewellery displayed in Room 32 will be transferred to Room 40.

ROOM 34 (Room of the altar)

No. **1495**. *The big altar*. This room houses dedications from ancient sanctuaries, especially outdoor shrines, with an altar in the centre. It is one of the type with simple fine lines and elegant volutes on the sides as the sole decoration. Three steps at the front were used by the priest when he prayed, and by the faithful who ascended them to lay their bloodless offerings on it. The altar was discovered in 1891 near the Theseion and, according to the inscription on the face of one of the sides, was dedicated by the Athenian People to Aphrodite and the Graces. *Circa* 210 B.C.

No. **1604**. *Torso of a statue of Aphrodite*. A number of attractive works from the sanctuary of Aphrodite at Daphni have been exhibited below the window in the south side.

Only the upper torso of the cult statue has been preserved; the goddess is leaning with her left elbow against a tree. The cult statue will have been a contemporary imitation of the "Aphrodite in the Gardens", which stood in a sanctuary in Athens and was the work of Alkamenes, the pupil of Pheidias. *Circa* 420 B.C.

No. **1597**. *Votive relief from Daphni*. This exceptionally fine relief was also dedicated in the sanctuary at Daphni. Aphrodite is depicted in the centre and Eros is standing on tiptoe on the palm of her left hand. The goddess is framed by other figures. *Circa* 420 B.C.

Nos. **4465-4466**. *Reliefs of Nymphs*. Two reliefs portraying Nymphs from the caves of Pentele are instructive for the spirit and ideal form of two centuries. In no. **4465** the figures, three exquisite Nymphs, Hermes and Pan, are calmly arranged in the shrine, which has such a fine crown, and are carved in low relief. In no. **4466**, which is in the form of a cave, the figures are set deep in the background and are carved in very deep relief, so that they stand almost like sculptures in the space. The inscription on the base reads: "Agathemeros dedicated (me) to the Nymphs". The first is a Classical work of about 360 B.C., and the second will have been produced half a century later at the end of the fourth century B.C. Both were probably dedications made by shepherds of the area.

No. 1966 Votive relief from the Cave of Pan

No. **1966**. *Votive relief*. A third period in the history of art is reflected in the third relief, which is much later and dates from about 100 B.C. The form of the shrine has become shapeless, with an inelegant crown, the relief elevation is slight, and the figures uneven. The scene is divided into two parts: on the left is Apollo, seated and bending over his *kithara*, and near to him is Hermes, in conversation with him. Both figures derive from earlier models carved in the round. The three Nymphs lack grace; they are holding hands, and are conventional, and their chitons are rendered in the archaising manner. On the right, behind a worshipper who is "adoring", other figures are traced in low relief. Even the small Pan on the extreme left has lost his Hellenistic freshness, and the sound of his pipes would have been lifeless.

No. **1462**. *Relief of Herakles from Eleusis*. The theme of Herakles feasting, familiar from earlier periods, is only associated with nature in Hellenistic art, when it becomes Dionysiac. This plaque from Eleusis (1881) is one of the most entertaining portrayals of the hero. He is lying on the ground on his lion skin, in the shade of a plane tree, his head turned upwards, as if singing. In his hand he holds a cup of wine, a little satyr behind him, playing the double flute, moves impulsively in the opposite direction. The useless club and quiver hang above and there is food on the ground, in front of Herakles.

Fragments of a copy of the same model – an Alexandrian work according to Jean Marcadé – have been found on Delos. However, the lack of tectonic structure suggests that the model may have been a painting, such as those on wooden panels dedicated by the worshippers in ancient sanctuaries. Although Herakles' body is rather flat, the centrifugal movement of the satyr dates the work to the late third or early second century B.C.

No. **683**. *Statuette of Pan*. The prayer of Socrates to Pan of the Ilissos, known from Plato's *Phaedrus*, is brought to mind by the few sculptures collected together on the north side of the altar, amongst which is the amusing statuette of Pan. He sits cross-legged on a rock on an animal skin, and will have been holding his shepherd's pipe in both hands. The piece was discovered in the Olympieion, but will have been dedicated in the shrine of Pan next to it, probably in the Hellenistic period.

No. **1455**. *Slab from Thespiai*. The heavy block of hard Boeotian stone, takes us out of the region of art to the rusticity of Askra, home of Hesiod. It comes from Thespiai, where the valley of the Muses was, and the bearded figure with dishevelled hair, projecting in low relief from the mountain, is a personification of Helikon. The lengthy inscription relates a nonsensical story, telling us that the block was dedicated by Amphikritos to the Muses and to Helikon; Hesiod is also mentioned.

ROOMS WITH WORKS FROM THE ROMAN PERIOD

Rooms 41-43 (Works from the Roman Period) are temporarily closed. In the pending re-arrangement of the Museum, the collection of terracotta figurines will be exhibited in Room 41 and various temporary exhibitions mounted in Rooms 42-45.

No. 4466 Relief of Nymphs. From Pentele

No. 683 Statuette of Pan

No. 1828 Statue of a Roman. From Delos

The Graeco-Roman art that made its appearance in a few representative works in the room of the Poseidon of Melos, reveals one side of its character in a greater number of examples in this room. First, however, let us remind ourselves of a few of the historical factors. From the battle of Pydna in 168 B.C. and the sack of Corinth by Mummius in 146 B.C., to the pillaging of Athens by Sulla in 86 B.C., there were thousands of incidents of plundering on no smaller scale than that of the infamous dicator, some of them organised by victorious generals, others unofficial in nature. Statues dedicated in sanctuaries were torn from their bases, as they were from the ancient agoras and elsewhere. The mist of slavery fell increasingly over the Greek province, this land of pain and suffering. Population decline, the diaspora of the artists, and the exodus to Rome were the consequences. These consequences, however, were not accompanied by the disappearance of all artistic activity in the Greek world. In Athens in particular, the distinction of the city's name, combined with a reverent devotion to the past, stimulated creativity, and during the second and first centuries B.C. there was no lack of orders from states or private individuals and "experts in the Greek voice" wishing the people who contributed to that city´s greatness to be honoured with a portrait. Nonethless, with the disappearance of the city-state, the full length statue, which had been erected in ancient times and showed a knowledge of the organic structure of the body and its movement, gradually fell into decline. It was athletics and "musical" education that had produced that unity of body and soul that was so incomparably expressed in Greek art.

Many of the Romans had imbibed Greek culture from the teachers of the diaspora, and had known at close hand the masterpieces plundered from Greece, and they continuously ordered copies of the other works that had remained *in situ* from the Athenian workshops. New figures and new styles, and the neo-Attic works with their refined skill, delighted the Romans, and many sculptors remained in Athens, where the profession existed and the Pentelic marble was to hand.

With the disappearance of the preconditions for the creation of new types of statue and the god-like youthful body, the bust now begins to be the most common form. The full length statues, whether honorific or funerary, were copies of Classical forms, in which the god's head was often replaced by a portrait head. The portrait heads in these rooms come from statues like these, or from autonomous busts. They attest, however, a fate that was not individual, particularly the ones that were produced before the Classicism of Hadrian (beginning of the second century A.D.), and they possess a spiritual drama foreign to the relentless "realism" of contemporaries in the rendering of the wrinkled melancholic face. The nobility and the expression of tragic isolation that hung heavily over these years derived from earlier centuries. We must not forget, however, that the phenomenon of the Roman portrait, "one of the most interesting in the history of the ancient world" (H. von Heintze), is missing from the Greek world throughout its entire history. There is no representation in Greek Museums of that startling series of Roman emperors. From the official coldness of Augustus, which Greek sculptors succeeded in combining with Classicism, from the burning undissembling figure of the soldier-emperor Trajan, to the paranoiac emperors like Nero, Calligula and Caracalla, we derive a picture not only of the progress of art, but also of Roman history and Roman civilisation. In the Greek world, where the Roman emperors were honoured with statues, often compulsorily, dedications to philhellenes (either statues or busts) were much more predominant; these were men who had inherited from Hadrian the custom of growing a beard, like the ancient philosophers. The Greek sculptures of this period, however, despite their provinciality, are not simply reflections of Roman art. They are something more: the expression of a life that was enacted and continued to be enacted in the enslaved province of Greece from the Late Hellenistic and Imperial periods to the end of the ancient world, when Phoebus no longer had his laurel and his hut and his prophetic water had lost its power, but when the national consciousness and the Greek language continued to live.

No. 368 Bust of the philosopher Metrodoros

ROOM 41

No. **985**. *Head of a poet*. (From the Karapanos Collection). This is a portrait of a poet without the slender band around his head; the short hair is rich, the forehead wrinkled, and the mouth is closed, while the relatively small eyes are looking upwards. It is a portrayal of an ill-humoured, critical character. This work presents a number of problems, because it undoubtedly depicts the "Pseudo-Seneca" who was so popular with the Romans, as is demonstrated by the great number of copies that have survived. They all derive from an original dating to the second century B.C., which depicted a coarse, contentious brusque poet, most probably Hesiod. The National Museum head does not belong to that type, full of Hellenistic exaltation, with the curls falling in disarray on the forehead, but derives from some other statue of the poet from the third century or end of the second century B.C., in which the features were much milder.

No. **368**. *Bust of the philosopher Metrodoros*. Bust of the philosopher Metrodoros, pupil of Epicurus, from Athens. A good, careful work from the second century A.D. or beginning of the third, which derives from an original statue from the first half of the third century B.C., which stood in Athens.

No. **706**. *The "marble woman"*. This is what she was called at the monastery of Loukous, where she was kept at the beginning of last century, and she was called "Amymone" by the first European travellers of that period. Along with other sculptures, the statue adorned the villa of Herodes Atticus in that picturesque site in Kynouria (Thyreatis). It will have been produced in an Athenian workshop to the order of Herodes Atticus. Second century A.D.

No. **1660**. *Funerary statue from Rheneia*. Incomplete funerary statue of a youth, from Rheneia. It is notably instructive for the different stages of the carving, and for the technique, which differed from that of Archaic and Classical sculptures. First century B.C.

ROOM 42

No. **219**. *Headless statue of a woman of the type the "Large woman of Herculaneum"*. This headless female statue was found in 1932

No. 325 Female portrait head

No. 3727. Archaising relief with the figure of Dionysos. From Chalandri

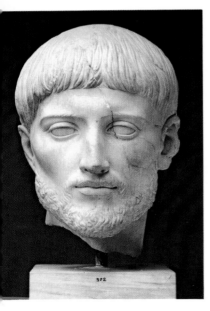

No. 372 Striking head from a funerary statue

at Palaiopolis on Andros, together with the Hermes (no. **218**, Room of the Diadoumenos), and it belongs to a funerary monument, probably of a man and wife. It is of the type of the "Large woman of Herculaneum", but the vigour of the carving, especially on the left side with the heavily shaded folds, demonstrates that it was no mechanical copy. Like the Hermes, the woman from Andros has been regarded as a product of the "neo-Parian" school of the first century A.D.; both statues are of Parian marble.

No. **1828**. *Statue from Delos*. Larger than life-size statue from Delos (house of the Diadoumenos), discovered in 1894. The heritage of Polykleitos has been adapted in the device of the chlamys wrapped in the right hand so that the edge of it can be put on the right shoulder. The hand, however, is supported on the side of the leg that is carrying the weight. *Circa* 50 B.C. It was once thought to be an athlete, but he must have been a propertied Roman, full of pride and most probably "un-Greek".

No. **1662**. *A statue of a victor from the Dipylon*. Incomplete statue of a youth on the point of adolescence, a victor, from the Dipylon. It was probably intended to stand on a grave. He is crowning himself with his right hand, and holding a palm frond in the other.

Nos. **325-26**. *Heads, male and female*. These two heads from a funerary monument, one female, the other male, were found at Minoa on Amorgos in 1888. The personal characteristics of the mature woman are mingled with traces of idealism. The delicate carving suggests the Late Hellenistic period, the first century B.C., but they more probably date from the first century A.D., and are part of the delicate Classicism that found its expression in the islands. Both figures are connected by the ivy crown they wear with the cult of Dionysos, who was worshipped in this area.

No. **515**. *Portrait head*. One of the most engaging portrait heads of the first century B.C. The wrinkled face has been suggested with soft chiselling and is in this way portrayed at peace giving an impression of kindness. The broad head of the bald sixty-year old, and the thick lower lip show that he was a Greek from the northern areas of the country, Epirus or Thrace. It was discovered in Athens.

No. **3561**. *Head of a young man*. This head of a slender, still young, man with a troubled expression, is a combination of influences from fourth-century B.C. heads and more recent elements. It possesses the nobility of Attic portrait heads of the period, but the man depicted may not have been a Greek; he may have been a Hellenised African or Syrian. First century B.C.

No. **320**. *Portrait head of a man from Athens*. Portrait head of a mature man, from Athens. The structure of the face is full of grooves and folds, and the expression is clouded by worry and a controlledd bitterness. The eyes are comparatively small, but the form possesses the Greek nobility and general sense of tragedy of the period. Second quarter of the first century B.C.

No. **3727**. *Relief with the figure of Dionysos*. The relief with the figure of Dionysos holding the *thyrsos* and the *kantharos* is of striking dimensions (height 1.61; width 0.90 m.) and is deceptive at first glance. One is inclined to consider it a neo-Attic archaising work of the first century B.C. The genuinely plastic nature of the body, however, and the dynamic rendering of the figure place it about the middle of the fourth century B.C., if not a little later – a Classical work, representative of the early archaising tendency. It was found at Chalandri in Athens in 1933.

No. **3625**. *Marble relief krater*. This marble relief krater, an important archaising work which is much later than the Dionysos from Chalandri, is adorned towards the top with a vine carved in low relief. The picture of the three *korai* holding hands and dancing, dressed in the archaic manner, is very attractive. The krater will have been a wellhead. First century B.C.

No. **3758**. *Portrait head of Augustus*. It has a broad scalp, with the formal parting of the curls above the forehead along its axis. From a statue which will have been erected in the Roman Agora of Athens (where it was found) in 20/19 B.C., when Augustus visited the city

No. **3606**. *Head of Lucius Caesar*. Portrait head of Lucius Caesar, grandson of Augustus. End of the first century B.C. or early years of the first century A.D.

No. **3665**. *Fragment from the head of Gaius Caesar*. Half of a portrait head of Gaius Caesar, the other grandson of Augustus. It was discovered in Kolokynthou in Athens. 20 B.C.- A.D. 4.

No. **328**. *Head of the Emperor Claudius*, from Smyrna. It differs from others portraying him in the dreaming eyes, which combine oddly with the stubborn expression that was foreign to his proneness to ill-health. First half of the first century A.D.

No. **345**. *Head of Domitian*. In this head of Domitian the sculptor has portrayed him with a short skull, and has at least succeeded in catching the gloomy expression of the universally hated emperor. Second half of the first century A.D.

No. **547**. *Head of a young girl from Smyrna*. The upper part of the head of a young girl from Smyrna. It has the incorporeality of the heads of the Julio-Claudian period. First half of the first century A.D.

No. **384**. *Bust of a mature man*. This bust from Eretria shows that the sculptor has attempted to render the personal features. It depicts a mature, slightly balding man, with no attempt to idealise him. End of the first or beginning of the second century A.D.

No. **372**. *Head from a funeral statue*. The charming head has an original plastic formation of the face, which is framed by the hair and the short beard. The expression of reflective grief suggests that it belonged to a funerary statue. First half of the second century A.D.

Copies of Classical Works. It is relatively rare that copies of large-scale Classical statues are discovered in Greece, though a large number of them adorn the museums of Italy and Europe. The poverty

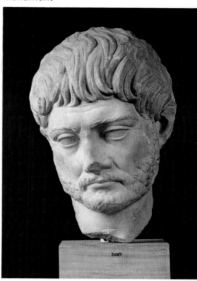

No. 3085 Head from a funerary monument

No. 3087 Female head from a funerary monument

93

No. 417 Bust of Antinoos

No. 420 Bust of a youth. From Phlious

of the country, the demotion of Greece to the rank of province, the destructions, the population decline and other causes were not favourable to the erection of these monumental works here. Most of them, however, were ordered by the Romans from Attic workshops, and they are so faithfully carved that they succeeded in passing on the Greek spirit and art not only to ancient Rome, but also to Europe from the Renaissance onwards.

No. **3890**. *The "thoughtful woman"*. One of the best of these statues, the "thoughtful woman", which is unfortunately headless, was discovered in Athens in 1941 during the war between Italy and Greece. It is of pure Pentelic marble, and will have been set up on the tomb of a woman. It is of the earliest type of *peplophoros*, but with a more recent development. It is not known whether the head had any representational features. Probably from the first century A.D.

Nos. **3085-3087**. *Heads from a funerary monument*. Three heads from a funerary monument of unknown type, which were discovered below the monument of Philopappos. The personal features have been idealised, in imitation of Attic grave reliefs of the Classical period. End of the first century A.D.

No. **3550**. *Bust of a young woman*. Bust of a young woman from the west slopes of the Acropolis. She is given an official character by the curl which rises above her forehead in the shape of a half-moon or anthemion. Beginning of the second century A.D.

Nos. **384-416**. *Stelai and heads of kosmetes*. The *kosmetes* of the ephebes, a title which occurs from as early as the fourth century B.C., is connected with the renewal of the institution of the ephebate about 334/3 B.C. According to Plato, the *kosmetes* had to be "a leader in music and gymnastics"; he had also to be fourty years old, and had many responsibilities.

A number of Herms, some of them inscribed, and heads of *kosmetes*, thirty-four in all, and all of them dating from the Imperial period, were found in 1861 in the ancient gymnasium, the Diogeneion (north slopes of the Acropolis), built into the later city walls.

The differences of character are more notable than the art, which is provincial, but they nonetheless reveal the ability to preserve the personality of the individual. These busts bring to life Athenian figures from the first century B.C. to the third A.D. The earliest seems to be the head no. **410**, with the broad skull, bald at the front, with no attempt at idealisation. It will antedate Hadrian and come from the end of the first century B.C.

Nos. **384, 386, 387, 385**. *Grave stelai*. The *stelai* of Heliodoros (no. **384**, beardless), Chrysippos (no. **386**), Onassos (no. **387**) and Sostratos (no. **385**) are preserved complete. Some of them, like the two most recent bearded figures, are in the form of ancient philosophers.

Nos. **390, 403, 393**. *Heads*. The head no. **390**, like no. **403**, depicts an aristocrat with a certain spirituality. No. **393** with an almost grim face and the long pointed beard has been likened to the head of Pan.

ROOM 43

No. **249**. *Bust of the Emperor Hadrian*. The bust of the Emperor Hadrian will have been erected in the Olympieion in Athens, where it was discovered in 1888 in the sanctuary that the philhellene emperor tried to restore. Beginning of the second century A.D.

No. **3729**. *Head of the Emperor Hadrian*. Large head of the Emperor Hadrian, set on a statue. Around the short hair is a rich crown of oak-leaves, and a central emblem (cameo?) above the forehead. The clear coldness of the face, which was foreign to the character of the philhellene emperor, shows that this Greek work was based on statues in Rome. It was found in Athens, in Syngrou Avenue (1918). First half of the second century A.D.

No. **350**. *Colossal head of the Emperor Lucius Verus*. The frontal view is emphasised in the striking colossal head of the Emperor Lucius Verus, adoptive son of Hadrian (A.D. 130-169), which was once set on a statue. The statue will have been erected in A.D,162 when Verus visited Athens.

No. **417**. *Bust of Antinoos*. The bust (along with a similar one, no. **418**) was found in 1887 in Patras, the city which was revitalised by the Greeks during the Imperial period. Both of them are portraits of Antinoos, the youth from Bithynia who caused such sleepless grief to the Emperor Hadrian when he was drowned in the Nile in October, A.D.130

Nos. **420, 2350**. *Portraits*. No. **420** from Phlious in the Peloponnese, is of the type of bust from the Hadrianic period, with its rather coarse, young face, and its head turned upwards (symbolising heroisation after death).
The one like it, no. **2350,** from Eleusis, is somewhat later, towards the middle of the second century A.D.; this also represents a naked youth, with no idealisation of the face.

No. **572**. *Head of Marcus Aurelius*. Head of Marcus Aurelius, from Athens, notable for the impressionistic rendering of the hair and beard that was usual during the reign of this emperor (A.D. 121-180).

No. **3563**. *Colossal head of the Emperor Antoninus Pius*. This colossal head of the Emperor Antoninus Pius, which was once set on a statue, is a purely Greek creation. Although the eyes, which were of a different material and were inlaid, are missing, the expression possesses a certain ancient grandeur that is almost god-like. The statue will have been erected in the temple of Apollo Patroios, or somewhere nearby, in the Athenian Agora, possibly after the deification of the emperor in A.D. 161.

Nos. **4819-4811**. *Busts of Herodes and Polydeukion*. These two busts were discovered in Kifisia, where Herodes Atticus had one of his villas. One of them depicts Herodes (no. **4810**), the other his favourite Polydeukion (no. **4811**), who died very young. Both busts from Kifisia are preserved intact, and constitute good examples of the genre from about the middle of the second century A.D.

No. 4810 Bust of Herodes Atticus

No. 419 Unique portrait head of a philosopher

No. **419**. *Portrait head of a philosopher*. The fact that so much has been written about this unique portrait head from a bust, is to be explained by its quality. The rendering of the thick hair by skilled use of the drill, and the contrast between it and the polished skin of the face constitutes a great sculptural achievement. Broad curls fall onto the shoulders, and the beard is not long. Most fascinating of all is the upward gaze, with a certain lack of symmetry in the eyes, and the harmonious curves of the eyebrows. The man portrayed was perhaps one of the many philosophers who taught in Athens at this period, A.D. 200. It was found in the theatre of Dionysos.

No. **1450**. *Relief of Polydeukion (?)*. This relief appears foreign, even though it has a classical shape. It was found at Loukous in Thyreatis. It is a matter of curiosity where a subject like this would have adorned the villa of Herodes Atticus. The snake is a chthonic element; curled around the tree, it is accepting food from the hand of the naked youth who is standing in front of his horse. Two birds are singing in the tree, and a small servant is running and holding out the helmet. The urn in the background is perhaps a suggestion of the ashes of the heroised man. Second century A.D. Perhaps the young man was one of the favourites of Herodes Atticus (Polydeukion?).

The Bronze Collection

The Bronze Collection of the National Museum is at once unique, charming and priceless, rich not so much in large-scale as in smaller and even miniature statues. Its value derives not only from the large quantity of statues and the lack of any stereotyped repetition, but also from the fact that the works possess a dazzling Greek quality. The eye is not clouded, as in so many foreign museums, by the intrusion of Etruscan or Roman works, and we can enjoy the artistic expression at its source. This was connected to a large extent with religion, for the bronze statues are not found so much in tombs, like the vases and figurines of clay; most of them come from ancient sanctuaries, where they had been dedicated by worshippers in fulfilment of a vow, or in the expectation of the favour of the deity. Each offered what he could, according to his profession and his belief. Many of the bronzes discovered on the Acropolis must have been dedicated by the bronze-smiths themselves to Athena Ergane.

A few of them, made in official workshops, reflect monumental works, but most of them are the products of simple craftsmen and therefore express more directly the feelings of the dedicators, and sometimes an amusing attempt to deceive the gods. Thus, a bronze statuette depicts an Arkadian shepherd carrying a heifer on his shoulder, which he had promised live to the god, and the same thing is shown by the large numbers of animals, oxen etc. from the Kabeirion in Boeotia. There are also, however, the portrayals of the gods themselves, of warriors, athletes, young men and women, Nikes,

No. 540 Statue of a woman wearing a peplos. From Pindos

97

sphinxes, and many others which were offered in order to gladden or to win the favour of a deity.

The nature of ancient religion contributed to a large extent to the great variety and to the personal choice of the dedicator as to the subject. Although moved by a deep religious feeling, the Greeks were not bound by theocratic rules and remained free to choose and shape their subject. The statuettes of the Archaic sixth century B.C. are gay, but become increasingly sober after 490 B.C. under the influence of the Classical spirit. It is their technique, above all, that makes the statuettes charming. It is true that the quality of a number of bronze statuettes is to be interpreted as reflecting the work of the great bronze-smiths of the Peloponnese — of Sparta, Argos, Corinth and Sikyon — but those from local workshops in more distant regions are not entirely without charm.

ROOM 36 (Karapanos Collection)

We have seen not only large-scale but also small bronze statues scattered throughout the sculpture rooms, but they are mainly collected together in the rooms beginning with the Karapanos room, in which nearly all the bronzes are from Dodona.

The Bronzes from Dodona

Konstantinos Karapanos, one of the patriots of Epirus who during the last century filled not only their suffering country but also the rest of Greece with gifts, presented the finds from his excavation at Dodona to the National Museum. However, antiquity smugglers took advantage of his absence to excavate secretly, and sold the biggest part of their finds to the Berlin Museum.

On a separate stand

No. **540**. Statue of a woman wearing a peplos, from Pindos. Circa 460 B.C.

Case 1: Sheet bronze plaques with oracles from Dodona

On a separate stand

Nos. **16547+27**. *Statuette of a small jockey.* The history of this is interesting. It was discovered during the excavations of Karapanos, and did not then have its horse. During the post-war excavations of Dem. Evangelidis the horse was discovered, and it was believed that the figure had been set upon it (as it is now). An examination of the traces in the National Museum workshops, however, established that this was not its position, and the thoughts of archaeologists turned immediately to a similar horse in the Louvre Museum, which came from the old clandestine excavations. Their suspicions were confirmed by a plaster cast. This was the position of the rider, as is shown in the illustration, where he is, correctly, leaning backwards to balance they way he is pulling on the reins. It remains now to find the second rider, who was mounted on the horse in the National Museum; he too will have been wearing the hat which is missing from the first rider. The two horsemen will have been cast in a Lakonian workshop and were without doubt the Dioskouroi, the brothers of Helen, and were dedicated to their father Zeus, to please him with their visit.

Nos. 27+16547 Statuette of a young horseman. From Dodona

Case 3: Discoveries from Dodona

No. **22**. Statuette of an ithyphallic Silenus. Excellent work of the second half of the sixth century B.C. The craftsmanship is also excellent in the repoussé plaque, no. **166**, with the two warriors. We can guess what this was used for: it will have been the cheek-piece of a very fine helmet.

On a separate stand

No. **16546**. Statuette of Zeus brandishing the thunderbolt, discovered during the post-war excavation. The base is also preserved; it was cast together with the statue and then fastened to a base of stone or wood. It is given a charming appearance by the patina, and also by its technique. The thunderbolt is connected to the head instead of starting from outside it, and the body is almost motionless and arranged around its axis. The right leg is not truly tensed.

Case 7: Discoveries from Dodona

Many of the bronze statuettes and plates are remains of large vases, cauldrons or official kraters with volute handles. The neck of one of these was adorned with the young rider (no. **36**), amongst other similar applied figures (sixth century B.C.). This has all the hallmarks of a Lakonian work, being full of life, and having a cheerful face, which is given a sense of action by the way the head is turned full face.

The runner, no. **24**, will have been set, full of life, on the rim of a large cauldron; this was also a Lakonian work.

No. **28**. Small bronze figurine of a seated male with a *pilos* on his head. It will have embellished the neck of a krater with volute handles, framing a representation, probably of warriors departing in chariots. Sixth century B.C.

In the same case the wonderful handle from a (Corinthian?) oinochoe no. **3783**, with a lion head at one end and a panther head at the other.

Case 4: Discoveries from several sites

No. **557**. Frying pan with handle in the shape of a naked youth. End of the sixth century B.C.

On a separate stand

No. **25**. Bronze statuette of a flute-player. End of the fifth century B.C.

Case 8: Discoveries from Dodona

The works we have seen so far were cast. The metal plaque depicting Skylla, no. **82**, was produced by a different technique – that of repoussé work. During this period (beginning of the fourth century B.C.) the hybrid form predominated, the upper part of the body being that of a woman; the face has a monumental beauty. To this body are attached two dogs and, behind them, the hooked tails of sea-monsters. The sea is indicated by curves below and Skylla is holding the helm, or an oar, in her left hand.

Bronze plaque with acroters. According to the inscription Agathon from Zakynthos dedicated it to Zeus.

The "weary Maenad", no. **19**, who is about to sink down after a dance, will have been either on or below the handle of an excellent Lakonian krater – a more recent work.

No. 16546 Statuette of Zeus throwing the thunderbolt. From Dodona

No. 19 The "Weary Maenad". From Dodona

Case 9: Discoveries from several sites

The statuette of a general, which was purchased after the war and almost certainly comes from Dodona, is unique (no. **16727**). The heads of the statuettes of generals from the Classical period survive only in copies, in the busts of the Roman period, and this piece therefore makes a significant contribution to our knowledge of this type of statue.

It was the opinion of Chr. Karouzos, who fought to acquire it for the National Museum that the general is depicted before the battle, holding in his hand the liver of divination which would predict his fortune in the battle to follow.

It is difficult to date the work — the second half of the fourth century B.C. is the latest probable period, though earlier dates cannot be excluded.

Nos. **784-794**. Chariot of the Roman period, imitating a Hellenistic type. Found at Nikomedeia in Asia Minor.

ROOMS 37-39 (Bronzes)

The bronze objects from rooms 37-39 are undergoing conservation and are thus not on display. Only part of room 37 is open to the public. Exhibited here are, in the main, small bronzes, arranged in cases according to their find spot.

Case 15:

No. **12831**. Statuette of a warrior (Achilles), from Karditsa. No. **15182**. Statuette of a hoplite. No. **11715**. Statuette of Athena Promachos and no. **14985**, figurine of a he-goat.

Case 17: Idaion Cave

Fibula no. **11765**.

Case 20: Boeotia

The famous Boeotian fibulae with catch-plate.

On a separate base

No. **16513**. Statuette of a flute-player wearing the characteristic sleeved chiton. On his head, the *phorbeia* to which the flute was attached. From the Heraion, Samos. 550-520 B.C.

Also exhibited in this sector of room 37 is no. **15118**, a bronze statue of Hermes (or a youth, probably an athlete from the palaestra, judging by the fillet around his head). This exceptional work, an old find brought up from the sea off Marathon in 1926, is close to the spirit of Praxiteles. It was evidently used as a lampstand in Roman times and most probably adorned the villa of Herodes Atticus, which the wealthy benefactor had built on his patrimonial land. The entire left arm and hand, wooden and with unarticulated fingers, are unworthy of the work and are a replacement to serve the new function. The combination of a very handsome head with the melodious curves of the body bespeaks the art and inspiration of a true artist. The contrapostal movement is imbued with intensity by the extension of the right arm.

All the harmonious lines of the sculpture suggest a mature creation

No. 16727 Unique statuette of a general. Probably from Dodona

No. 166 Cheek-piece of a bronze helmet from Dodona

101

No. 6440 Bronze head of Zeus

No. 6444 Part of a larnax (chest)

of Praxiteles. It was he who gave this form to the god who, though swaddled by his mother in Kyllene, developed with slender elegance in Athens, in the Late Classical art of the fourth century B.C.

Of the other bronzes formerly on show in rooms 37 and 40, the most important are mentioned below in the manner in which they were exhibited prior to their removal for conservation.

Case 10: Discoveries from Olympia

A number of apparently unimportant statuettes from the Late Geometric period, showing a figure raising its hands on high, have been interpreted as depicting the "Zeus in Epiphany" of Olympia. These are local, unpretentious works. A charioteer wearing a helmet (no. **6190**) of Geometric type, and standing in his chariot, is also from a workshop in Elis.

The statuette of Zeus (?) wearing a helmet is also Geometric; it is probably a local work (no. **6178a**).

The large bust of a bull, no. **6158**, was worked in the old repoussé technique of the seventh century B.C. It is not certain that it adorned an enormous cauldron, like some of the huge, fabulous ones discovered in the post-war excavations.

The worshipper from the eastern part of the Aegean will have offered to a goddess of the Altis either a tripod cauldron or a *perirrhanterion*, which was supported by the female figure no. **6149**, wearing the Ionic chiton, and by other figures. The whole work, which will undoubtedly have been produced in a Samian workshop at the beginning of the sixth century B.C., had the rounded form of a column, and the face has an expression of eastern impassivity.

Nos. **6213**, **6241**. Two charming little horses of the Late Geometric period.

Nos. **7941**. Phoenician *phiale*.

No. **7483**. Handle of a large Geometric tripod.

Case 11: Discoveries from Olympia

Bronzes of the Archaic period from Olympia.

On a separate stand

No. **6440**. *Head from a statue of Zeus.* The god is portrayed with a "wedge-shaped beard" and an austere, divine expression. The hair is arranged in two successive rows on the narrow forehead and drawn into a "knot" behind, held in place by two broad bands, ringlets falling on the chest. The work, discovered in 1877, is one of the earliest cast statues from a Corinthian atelier. 520-510 B.C.

On a separate stand

No. **6163**. *Statuette, perhaps of Zeus.* The artist who made this small statue took it from one of the statues wearing a himation, possibly depicting Zeus in a peaceful pose. It is from the last decade of the sixth century B.C. and comes from a north Peloponnesian workshop.

On a separate stand

No. **6444**. *Part of a larnax (chest).* The large repoussé plaque is part of a rich dedication – perhaps a larnax (chest). This is also the

No. 15118 The "Marathon boy", a bronze statue recovered from the sea off Marathon

achievement of an Ionian workshop. It is divided into four bands placed vertically above each other, the broadest at the bottom depicting winged Artemis, the Mistress of the animals; above her, Herakles is shooting the Centaur, and the two upper bands with decorative motifs.

Case 12: Discoveries from Olympia

No. **6192**. Excellent statuette of a half-reclining komast from the rim of a cauldron. No. **6086**. Statuette of a kore. No. **6230**. Statuette of a lion. No. **6235**. Statuette of a sphinx with two faces. Nos. **6236**. Small figurine depicting seven women. They are arm-in-arm, dancing a circular religious dance, and the object is a dedication to one of the female deities of the Altis (Hera, Eilithyia, Aphrodite or Artemis). Local work.

Case 9: Discoveries from several sites – Boeotia

Turning to the items exhibited in the other cases, we may examine the famous Boeotian fibulae with plaques incised with animals, birds, ships, and also mythological subjects, amongst which the Theban Herakles is most frequent. Their dating to the end of the eighth century B.C., and the attribution of a good number of them to Boeotian craftsmen are both well-founded, though similar fibulae are found in the Peloponnese. No. **8602**. Bronze belt from Plataea. Middle of the fifth century B.C.

On a separate stand

No. **16512**: *Spout of a spring*. The unique and very diverting bronze on a separate stand, was the spout of a spring; a frog is "waiting" for the water, seated firmly on the lion's head. It was found in the Samian Heraion and demonstrates the playful inventiveness of the bronze-smiths of the seventh century B.C.

Case 13: Discoveries from Thessaly – Phthiotis

The ancient gods were very receptive and accepted even the humblest dedications. This miniature fibula and the little birds in this case came from Thessalian shrines. Late Geometric.

On a separate stand

No. **12831**. *Statue of a warrior*. Thessaly, distant as it was from the artistic centres of bronze-working in this period, naturally produced works that were peculiar to the area and not altogether pleasing. Nonetheless, the statuette of a hoplite, from Karditsa, is interesting. It is preserved complete with all its equipment. A belt is fastened round his waist, and below it the male member has been shown with some emphasis. A shield of Boeotian type hangs from his back, and in his hands he will have been holding the shield and spear. A primitive helmet-cum-hat covers the head.

The overlong body indicates that he is a mythical figure, and the statuette probably depicts a hero from the epic – and who other than Achilles, whose home, Phthia, was not far from Karditsa? The probable date of this unique work is the first half of the seventh century B.C.

Case 14: Discoveries from several sites

One of the best exhibits in the next case is the baldric, no. **16514**, from the region of Asea in Arkadia. It even has the vertical spits to

No. 12831 Statuette of a hoplite. From Karditsa, Thessaly

hold the clasps – a rare piece of fortune which leaves no doubt as to the function of this bronze plate. It is not known whether the warriors are figures from the epic. Two men have dismounted from their chariots and are engaged in single combat; on the left a charioteer is carrying a Boeotian shield, and the figure in the centre of the baldric is another standing warrior.

The craftsman has given movement to their legs and bodies, and the inheritance of the Geometric figures gives a lively feeling to the repoussé belt, which belonged to a warrior who will have lived in the first half of the seventh century B.C., and was perhaps buried in Arkadia. Next to it are the two, almost ugly, Thessalian statuettes, no. **15182** of a hoplite, and no. **11715** of Athena Promachos. This is inferior and very rustic work, which will have been produced about the middle of the sixth century B.C., if not earlier. The elegant figurine of a wonderful goat with horns (they are not exactly curved horns), no. **14985**, is much more attractive. This is also from Thessaly.

The sheet-bronze plaque, no. **7550**, depicts a slim warrior affixing his greave to his raised left leg. He wears a Corinthian helmet and his hair falls down his back. This is an excellent piece, probably from a Lakonian workshop, dating from about 540 B.C. Found in Edessa, it was probably attached to the neck of a "Lakonian" krater with volute handles.

No. **7492** is the handle of a rather small tripod. It and its horse finial are of cast bronze.

On a separate stand

No. **6446**. *Head of warrior*. The well known warrior's head has survived from a life-size statue. The overall effect suffers from the loss of the helmet, but the structure of the face, and the technique generally, remain intact, and date it roughly to the period of the warrior's heads from the later, eastern pediment of the temple of Aphaea of Aegina. *Circa* 490 B.C. From Karditsa, Thessaly.

Case 15: Discoveries from the Peloponnese

The group of small bronzes, nos. **13053-13155**, transports us to a verdant rural shrine of Pan outside of Olympia (site of Berekla).

The charming kouros no. **13056**, carrying a cock as a gift, is wearing a radiate crown of leaves. The three insignificant pieces of metal in the shape of a simple mirror were humble dedications by women. The statuette no. **13060** gives a delightful picture of a shepherd – the man who dedicated it in the same shrine. It is a local product and reflects Corinthian work in the clear lines of the face. Wrapped in his heavy cloak, he is wearing a hat to protect himself against the snow of the Arkadian mountains. Another shepherd (no. **13053**) is more lightly dressed in a short chiton; he has a heifer on his shoulder – a miniature picture of the man who had vowed to dedicate it to the god. As for the picture of the hanging fox (no. **13054**), Tsountas used to ask in his classes if it were the dedication of a farmer who had caught the destructive animal, or if it were the expression of a prayer: "may I see it hanging thus".

The bronze statuette of a naked, bearded warrior, no. **14765**, from Arkadia, is humble but interesting; it was originally fastened to a base. The form of the tall helmet, well known from portraits of Pericles, has led to the theory that it was the Athenian general who was pictured in this small work. It undoubtedly derives from some larger model that will have depicted him heroised.

No. 6446 Large head of a bearded warrior

No. 13056 Charming kouros

105

No. 6476 Bronze statuette of a Nike. From the Acropolis

The two statues of Hermes were found in Andritsaina. No. **12348** is plain with a short chiton and flat hat, whereas the ram-bearer, no. **12347**, is quite wonderful with his winged sandals and pointed hat topped by a lotus blossom. He will have held a caduceus in his left hand. Work of a local bronze-smith of the second half of the sixth century B.C., if not slightly earlier.

Case 16: Discoveries from Boeotia

The charming statuette of the "*anthesphoros*" *kore*, no. **7388**, from the Ptoion, takes us into the sphere of monumental art; it is a Boeotian work from the middle of the sixth century B.C., but is influenced by Attic *korai*. No. **7384**. The protomes of two "Sirens", which were attached to the rim of a cauldron, were preserved with two remnants from its repoussé body. The hand, as well as the ideals, of an Argive bronzesmith can clearly be seen in the small *kouros* no. **7382**, which is also from the sanctury of Apollo Ptoios. In the lower part of the case there is a selection of bronze and lead animals, votive offerings from the Boeotian Kabeirion.

No. **7412**. Important statuette of a discobolos from, the Ptoion. Fifth century B.C.

On a separate stand

No. **14984**. *Zeus Keraunobolos from Ambrakia*. The Zeus from Ambrakia is bigger than the known statuettes of Zeus Keraunobolos (height 0.165m; with pedestal 0.188m.). The greenish patina has been well preserved.

Bronzes from the Acropolis

A significant event in world history, the sacking of the Acropolis by the Persians, was the basic reason for the preservation of a large number of splendid works in marble and bronze — the latter of many types and from many periods.

In 480 B.C., the year of the battle of Salamis, the Persians plundered the Acropolis along with the city of Athens, and threw down all the statues, cult and votive, all of them brilliant creations of Archaic art. When the Athenians returned to their homes after the famous victory and discovered the holy dedications torn from their bases, being reverent and full of gratitude to the gods, they did not think of throwing them away. Instead they buried them in the bosom of the rock, where they remained guarded for many centuries, until they were revealed by the excavations on the Acropolis in 1885-1890. Many bronzes were also buried in this "pre-Persian" level, as well as a large number of fragments of very fine vases (a selection may be seen on the second floor). Most of the finds date from the years 520-480 B.C.

A single glance at the cases holding the bronzes from these excavations is enough to reveal the variety of the dedications and the varied nature of the evidence they supply: little horses, statuettes of warriors, figures from tripod cauldrons, spears and other weapons, small *kouroi*, athletes, all kinds of animals, griffins from the rims of cauldrons, bases of vases, busts with *korai* carrying flowers, flying Victories, and, naturally, statues of Athena Promachos. On one small shield we may read the inscription: "Phrygia the bread-seller dedicat-

No. 6479 Bronze statuette of a Nike. From the Acropolis

No. 6445 Statuette of a naked wrestler. From the Acropolis

106

No. 6597 Kouros

ed (me)". A poor barbarian maid had dedicated it to Athena. A small bronze boat has the following dedicatory inscription incised on it: "(I am) sacred to Athena".

On a separate stand

No. **6445**. *Naked wrestler.* One of the largest statuettes from the Acropolis, the well known naked wrestler. It has the form of a *kouros* with the left leg thrust forward, but the arms are free and the left one is dynamically separated from the body. He will have held dumb-bells in his tightly closed palms. His step is light and his face looks radiantly ahead; his hair is short, as in the later *kouroi*, but the pubic hair is not shown. *Circa* 500 B.C.

No. **6448**. *A statuette of Athena* consisting of two bronze-sheet plaques stuck together. The goddess wears a chiton, himation and the aegis. The folds are gathered between her legs and the feet are bare. She has a diadem on her head. Traces of gilding on the best preserved face. It is not known what she held in her hand, since only one arm is shown on each plaque. Late sixth century B.C.

No. **6449**. The lower part of a similar plaque, which will have been affixed somewhere, opposite the preceding one.

On the wall

No. **6635**. *Head of a griffin.* The head of a griffin from a tripod cauldron is unexpected: it is evidence or the progress made in the art of large cast bronze works.

Case 18: Discoveries from the Acropolis

Half of a herald's wand, the customary staff of Hermes (no. **7146**), carries a moving reminder of the struggles of the Athenians for freedom. The picture of Pan, which will have had a similar one to balance it, is one of the oldest found in Athens, and demonstrates the gratitude of the Athenians to the Arkadian goat-god who spread panic in the Persian army, even though he complained that the Athenians did not recognise him and had not honoured him until then. It is not known whether the herald's wand belonged to a statue of Hermes, or whether it was set in the hand of Iris, who was also a messenger of the gods. We may be certain that it was not in the "Persian level", but will have been made about 470 B.C.

The *kore* no. **6491**, on a triangular base, seems out of place amongst the Acropolis *korai*. The fleshless body, the flat shape, the lifeless face and the whole effect are reminiscent of terracotta Corinthian figurines, and this *kore* must also be a Corinthian work. The derivation of the way the fluted ἔμβολον above her head terminated is unknown.

Nos. **6475, 6476, 6480, 6479, 6478**. *Nikai.* The large number of Nikes (Victories) will have been attached to vessels. Bringing joy to the goddess, they fly with bent knees, each one different, with their wings bow-shaped, or more rarely sword-shaped, as in the best of all of them, no. **6477**, with the skilled rendering of the folds of the garment. Some of them are holding the edges of their dress in order to fly less encumbered and announce the victory which "κατέχει τὸν βίοτον" of good men.

Case 21: Discoveries from the Acropolis

The statuettes of *kouroi* wearing "slippers" will have been dedicated by humble worshippers. One of these, no. **6598**,. with its double

No. 6457 Statuette of Athena

base, will have been holding dumb-bells in his hands, while another, no. **6597**, will have had a phiale for making a libation in his right hand. The gentle sweetness of the face is reminiscent of Ionic works, and the knot of hair falling on the back is charming. Both statuettes will have been produced about 490 B.C. The Corinthian features are unmistakable in the contemporary statuette no. **6600**. It depicts Hermes as a wayfarer, with the chlamys thrown over his shoulder and hat on head, accommodating and smiling.

The successful connection of the discobolos (no. **6615**) to its base established the correct interpretation of this figure, which had previously been thought to be a dancer. 490-480 B.C.

The movement of another exceptionally fine discobolos, no. **6758**, will have been explosive; only the arm has been preserved, with the discus held tightly in the spread fingers.

Case 19: Discoveries from the Acropolis

A fair number of smaller statuettes are of the same type as that of Athena, and though they are smaller works of art, they do not omit even the aegis. The craftsman who made one fine work of Athena, no. **6457**, found the aegis difficult, and preferred to continue the himation above half the breast. He depicted her with all her other weapons – helmet, shield, and spear – in her right hand. The legs are bare of any folds (which are gathered together only in the middle in a somewhat archaic fashion) and have a false form, and the wonderful face has a god-like silence. The statue is intended to be viewed mainly from one angle, and the rear of the body has been neglected. It probably dates from shortly before 480 B.C.

The creator of the Athena no. **6451**, which is contemporary with the preceding one, was even more eccentric and deprived her of the himation. The sleeved chiton is tight around the breast and is girded in such a way as to separate off the lower body, which is narrow but has a harmonious curve in the right leg. It is not clear how the statuette was attached to its base. The particular interest of it is that the artist abandoned the folds, and instead used wavy incised lines to give a very skilful suggestion of them.

The headless statuette of Athena no. **6454**, which is the most dazzling of them all, recalls the dawn of Pheidian art. It differs from the others in that she holds a spear in her right hand and what is perhaps an owl, or something else, in her left. The garments have no folds, and she is framed by the strong verticals that cover the left leg.

The fold of the Lakonian-Ionian peplos reveals rather than covers the curves of the upper body. The bronze-smith has retained the form of the aegis from the earlier statues; it is short in front, but hangs low at the rear (as in the Athena of Meleso) and follows the curves of the body. The scales of the aegis have been engraved wth amazing patience. One would think that the mature Athena came from the hand of a great bronze-smith who was one of the creators of the Classical style. It will have been cast about 460 B.C.

The horses nos. **6539** and **6544** are two of the earliest of these works and date from the Geometric period; the mane and the chest are curved and the light body narrow, as in the phase of the Geometric style about the middle of the eighth century B.C. They were not separate dedications, but will have stood as decorations above the handles of a cauldron. The interesting figures nos. **6628**, **6449**, **6538** and **6777** had a similar function. These are the earliest figures, and

No. 6519 Winged daemon

No. 6511 Part of the base of a bronze tripod. An Etruscan work

No. 6626 Youth on a dolphin; a vase attachment

are dated to the end of the eighth century B.C. on the basis of their long thin bodies.

The same phase of early Archaic art is represented by the winged spirit no. **6519**. This is cast in bronze and was set on the rim of a cauldron of the usual type, but which was exceptional in its peculiar outer surface, with the levels separate and almost linear. There is an incision underneath the figure in the shape of an X, and if this is not accidental it may help to attribute this work to a particular workshop, for it is known as the letter E of the Sikyonian alphabet, and of this alphabet alone. The style is related to figures on Protocorinthian vases from the first half of the seventh century B.C., and does not conflict with the attribution to a Sikyonian workshop.

The *kouros* no. **6619** belongs to the pure "Daedalic" phase of the art in the middle of the seventh century B.C.; it was probably a separate dedication. A good example of a "Daedalic" face is preserved in the bust no. **6627**, in which the face projects more than is usual in Daedalic works.

No. **6613**. Statuette of a warrior. Late Geometric period.

Case 23: Discoveries from the Acropolis

The busts of "*anthesphoroi* " *korai* will have decorated the rims of vases; no. **6470** is most attractive, as is the flower no. **6527**. The slender-bodied *kouroi* with feet joined together are remains of frying pans dedicated in the shrines on the Acropolis. One, no. **6566**, is standing on the skull of a ram.

The vase-handle with three figures and the remains of a fourth is out of place amongst the Attic works. The figures are Herakles, a flute-player, another figure and Hermes (no. **6511**).

The busts of Pegasus (no. **6673**) were used to enliven the handles of plates-plaques and are amongst the finer achievements of bronze art.

The *kore* mirror handle no. **6504+6549** is distinctive amonst the female figures. It is the only Attic example of this Peloponnesian type, which did not become established in Athenian workshops. It was only after the war that it was connected with its base, a type of chariot pulled by two small horses. She is holding a flower in each hand and her body narrows downwards; it is interrupted by the fold of the chiton, while the folded chlamys makes a diagonal across the breast. The face, with its stern thoughtful expression, has the form of the Severe Style. *Circa* 470 B.C.

The liveliness added to the rims of bronze vessels by the small figures can be seen from the Centaur no. **6580** (others like him will have been running round the rim as though drunk from the smell of the wine), and the slinger no. **6630**.

The youth on a dolphin, no. **6626**, will have been emerging like a swimmer from the wine in the vase.

The accounts of the treasurers have been incised on the plaque no. **6975**, in Archaic script; we are now entering another period, when the Athenian democracy controlled the cataloguing and management of the dedications on the Acropolis: "οἱ ταμίαι τάδε χαλκία…" (The treasurers (paid) this to the bronze-smith).

On separate stands

Nos. **6447**, **16758**. *Statuettes of Athena Promachos*. In contrast

Nos. 6504+6549 Kore, mirror handle

No. 6447 Statuette of Athena Promachos, dedicated be Meleso

No. 11691 Bronze mirror

with other sanctuaries, at Olympia and Delphi, there was never any Panhellenic participation in the sanctuaries on the Acropolis, with the result that, with a few exceptions, the dedications are Attic, and it is our knowledge of Attic art that is enriched by the finds on the sacred rock.

The statuettes in the form of Athena Promachos, above all else, were undoubtedly the special property of Athena. They begin quite early, before 550 B.C., and they stop about 480 B.C. The model for the pure type of Promachos was the statue erected at the time of the renewal of the Panathenaia in 566 B.C., in the archonship of Hippokleides. Most of the statuettes are later, however, and are not faithful copies, but show certain deviations from that statue.

The best and most complete idea of the type of Promachos is given by the latest statuette, dedicated to Athena by an otherwise unknown woman, Meleso (no. **6447**). The base also survives: it will have been affixed to a wooden or marble pedestal.

Two dresses can be distinguished below the himation, which has folds down to the knees; she is covered behind by the long aegis, which reveals the curve of the back. The scales of it are indicated by incised lines. In front it is short and covers part of the breast, and it appears that it was covered with gold. The very high crest of the Attic helmet is derived from the neck of a swan. The whole statue is intended to be seen from one main angle. The apparent conflict between the stern face, which dates the work to about 470 B.C., and the archaic schematisation of the folds between the legs, is to be explained in terms of an archaising tendency that is easily comprehensible in a derivative work.

The excellent quality of this statuette is even more apparent if it is compared with a statuette of the same type that is an imitation of the same model (no. **16768**, on a separate column); it is larger and had a richer rendering of the folds. It was found near Desphina in Phokis. The craftsman, however, probably a Boeotian, did not possess the sensibility of the man who worked the statuette of Meleso, and the aegis is undecorated in front and at the rear. It is interesting that the Acropolis statuette was used as a model in such a distant sanctuary.

Case 20: Bronze mirrors

One of the most appealing branches of ancient bronze art consists without doubt of the mirrors, particularly when the reflecting disc is set on the heads of maidens or goddesses. In the metal, which originally had a shiny surface, ancient women looked at their faces, combed their hair, beautified themselves, and then hung up the mirror or put it aside on the table. The disc is always perfectly circular, because it was believed that the mirror had a magic connection with the moon; on a vase whose traces are now lost, Thessalian witches are shown trying to bring down the moon with the magic of the mirror.

We shall get to know the various types of mirrors in the local workshops and centres of bronze-working not only in the following pages (here from the sixth century B.C.), but also in the description of the bronzes in the room to the left of the great staircase leading to the second floor.

It would be strange if at Corinth, the home of bronze-working, the bronze-smiths had not become specialists in making mirrors at an early date. The ones surviving from the second half of the sixth century B.C. have a simple, though not undecorated form. There were relief figures on the square plaque attached to the disc, and also on the long narrow handle below it; there are other mirrors of this type surviving that are undecorated (nos. **16508**, **7691**, **7687**).

It seems that it was bronze-smiths from Sparta, basing themselves on Egyptian models, who were the first to attempt to set the disc of the mirror on the head of a female figure. One of the earliest, the small mirror from Leonidi in Kynouria, has the disc connected to the *polos*, the head covering that indicates that the figure is a goddess (no. **7465**). She can be no other than Helen in her capacity as goddess, who protected female beauty and knew how to transform ugliness. *Circa* 560 B.C. The mirror from Aegina, no. **7703**, undoubtedly of local workmanship, is only a little later. The young maiden, who is standing on tiptoe on a turtle, is wearing a light kilt; in her raised hands she is holding the ends of the volutes of a column capital that forms the transition to the disc. The key to the interpretation of this figure, which is reminiscent of similar maidens on Egyptian mirrors, is supplied by the kilt: she must be a harlot, a dancer or a tumbler, and not a goddess. The inventive bronze-worker wanted to portray an acrobatic game.

A favourite subject of Lakonian workshops, the naked cymbal-player, can be seen in the maiden from the Amyklaion in Sparta, no. **7548**. It is later than the "Helen" of the mirror nearby and reminds one of a number of imaginative Lakonian maidens which are amongst the best Lakonian bronzes of the sixth century B.C. The Corinthians, however, developed more fully the form of the *korai* supporting the reflecting disc. The *kore* no. **11691**, from a mirror which has survived complete, is rich and striking. There are sphinxes standing on her shoulders and supporting the disc with one leg; the whole figure, which is of the type of the "Ionic" *kore* from the Acropolis, and indeed the whole mirror, is a masterpiece by a skilled bronze-worker of about 520 B.C. Another type of figure can be seen in the more recent kore no. **7464**. She is not wearing the himation, and since the fold of the chiton falls low, the lower body is shown fore-shortened. She is wearing slippers which, along with her whole presence and style, favours the attribution to a Sikyonian workshop. *Circa* 500 B.C.

The next stage was the "*peplophoros*" *kore* – a type of mirror support of which we shall see excellent examples in the room to the right of the staircase.

The *kore* mirror handle did not establish itself in Athens. Here the preference was for a simple disc with a handle of wood, ivory or simply bone. The artists sought beauty in other devices – in the curling anthemia which were cast together with the disc and formed the transition between it and the handle. The mirror disc no. **11350**, from a tomb in Athens (beginning of the fifth century B.C) is still heavy. Later they lose the curling anthemia and this austere harmony and precision, and become more slender (no. **7690**). In place of the anthemia, a Siren is in attendance as the beautiful woman looks at her reflection, as in the mirror no. **16509**, with its Attic limpidity.

Case 24: Discoveries from the Peloponnese

In this case are some of the best bronze statuettes of the sixth century B.C. The distinctive Spartan warrior is one of the best Lakonian products (no. **14789**). He is wearing the Corinthian helmet with

No. 14921 Plaque with Persephone

113

very high crest, a chiton with engraved decoration, and the Archaic bell-shaped breast-plate which has the outline of the anatomy of the body and reaches only to his waist. Unspeaking and austere, he calls to mind the military poems of Tyrtaios. The same type of breast-plate can be studied in the other, smaller Lakonian statuette of the hoplite Karmos (no. **7598**), from Aghios Kosmas in Kynouria. According to the inscription incised on the base, it was dedicated by Charillos to Apollo Maleatas. The small statuette no. **7614**, from Phoinike in Lakonia, has an attractive subject: a naked man with a short beard is carrying a hydria. The bronze *kouros* torso no. **7533**, with the curls falling over the shoulders and back, was also found at Phoinike.

Arkadia produced a number of notable works in a variety of types. The Palladion from Tegea, no. **14828**, wearing her panoply, all of which has been preserved, is of a type which many decades later (more precisely at the end of the sixth century B.C.) was to develop and become established in Athens as the type of Athena Promachos. The out-turning metal plate no. **14921** was also found at Tegea. It depicts Persephone, Kore, dressed in chiton and himation, holding in her hands a phiale and a torch. Judging from her austere face and her dress, we should date her about 470-460 B.C. In contrast, no. **7605**, the *peplophoros* who is pouring a libation (possibly a goddess), is depicted as a country-woman from Arkadia; this is also from Tegea. *Circa* 470 B.C. The local craftsman who made no. **7565** attempted to differentiate between the legs of the moving figure, making the left one relaxed. (*Circa* 430 B.C.). The statuette of the lyre-player (there is no doubt that this is what he was, even though the lyre is missing), no. **14811**, is not as unimportant as it appears. Comparing it with others of the same type, researchers have named it Orpheus, and have suspected that these statuettes, like a head in Munich, give an idea of a famous work by Dionysios of Argos which was dedicated at Olympia.

The fact that important works of art were dedicated even in the most distant and unapproachable sanctuaries is not inexplicable if one considers the position held by art in Greece and its connection with religious observances. Nonetheless, the exceptionally fine statuette of a seated Zeus holding the thunderbolt, no. **13209,** must have been an unexpected find for the archaeologist who arrived at the peak of the Arkadian mountain Lykaios. It is probably from a workshop in Corinth, the home of bronze art. The beard is pointed, and the glance lively; the waving folds of the long chiton are incised, while those of the himation, folded diagonally across the chest, are in relief. The throne on which Zeus was sitting is missing. The interesting bronze statuette from Lykaios probably dates from the end of the sixth century B.C. No. **14922**. Statue of Persephone sitting on a high seat (throne). Beautiful Peloponnesian work. *Circa* 450 B.C.

Case 26: Bronze mirrors

The type of the *kore* mirror handle that we met in the other room of the bronzes is continued by the later *korai* of the fifth century B.C.

Apart from the pleasure they give, they offer valuable evidence for the contemporary large scale statues, the *peplophoroi*, which were the creation of the renowned bronze-smiths of the central and northern Peloponnese. Since the type of *kore* wearing the Ionic chiton had not established itself there, and as contact with Ionian luxury had not

No. 16111 Silver cover of a folding mirror

Detail (head) of the "Marathon boy" (No. 15118)

intruded into the ancient Doric ideal of the human figure, these were the first men to create new types of female statues. They went beyond the Archaic shapes and faced the problem of producing a balanced movement, which they achieved in the female statue by the use of the Doric peplos.

The leg thrust forward is now balanced by the relaxed arm, each statue having a different gesture. *Kore* handles of this type reached as far as Athens. The mirror no. **7579**, with all its fittings, was found in a woman's tomb in the neighbourhood of Kypseli. This *kore* is a happy translation on a smaller scale of a monumental *peplophoros* — probably the work of an Argean bronze-smith imitated by a skilled fellow-countryman. The *kore* is wearing the Argean type of Doric peplos, which is girded, with the bosom seen beneath the hanging fold. The fold of it falls vertically on the left leg, on which the weight is resting, and the other leg is only slightly relaxed.

It was perhaps at Argos that the motif of the hand supported on the hip was first devised, and then deployed in the new Classical pose of the body. The remains of the fresh Archaic imagination can be seen in the hares running round the mirror disc and amongst the leaves (conventionally indicated in the shape of rosettes), and also in the two cocks facing each other on top. During this period, a balance was achieved for the first time between the *kore* and the size of the mirror disc, which in earlier times was bigger and difficult to support. The small additional parts were cast separately, including even the Cupids flying above her. We may recall the heavy sphinxes in the same position on the Archaic mirrors. Only the system of anthemia that connects the figure of the *kore* to the mirror disc was cast together with it. The *kore* might be thought of as Aphrodite in view of the Cupids, and indeed as a successor of the Helen of the Lakonian mirror (no. **7465**). But these winged spirits might reasonably accompany any maiden when she was beautifying herself in front of the metal disc. The Cupids regularly fly toward the outside at this period, while in the immediately succeeding phase they change direction and fly towards the middle, as in the *kore* handle no. **7576**, with their hands extended in blessing above her head. The Cupids here are now young boys rather than children.

The disc of this mirror is still large, though it is devoid of the decorations that the other mirror has, and the way it is successfully balanced on her head is wonderful. If she has to be called Aphrodite, this is not so important as the subject and the way she is dressed. She is wearing the Ionian-Lakonian peplos, without the bosom. The device of the left hand hidden behind the overhanging fold is probably not that of the bronze-worker. Together with the whole stance it echoes some large-scale work by a bronze-smith, who was perhaps from Corinth or Sikyon, rather than Argos.

Between the two mirrors is another *kore* kandle, no. **16517**. This came from a humbler work, but it is interesting for the rare subject, which was probably the tasteful device of a craftsman rather than an important artist. She is holding the mirror in one hand, and straightening her hair with the other, as the owner of the mirror would have done.

Folding mirrors. Another type of mirror, the so-called folding mirror, makes its appearance before the end of the fifth century B.C. The disc is no longer supported on a female figure, but has a cover which is ornamented with repoussé figures in relief. As the fourth century advances, the cover becomes bigger and the theme more

No. 7576 Bronze mirror with Aphrodite and Cupids

narrative. It would be bold to connect the works with the names of famous craftsmen of this period, but the best of them reflect the activity of these men, even though they are the work of simple technicians. It is believed that the change to the new type of mirror occurred in the workshops of Athens and Corinth, though there are some indications that the first steps were taken in Athens. Mys, who worked on the figures on the shield held by Athena Parthenos, is the earliest repoussé worker referred to by the later historians of ancient art.

The earliest known mirror, with a cover for both sides, nos. **7417-7418**, was discovered in Eretria in 1891: there is no need, however, to regard it as a work from Chalkis — Athens has greater claims on it. At this early stage the cover did not hide the whole of the disc, and the relief figures are rather small, attention being paid more to the decoration of the rim. There is a single beautiful figure on each side: A) Aphrodite riding on the swan, B) Selene on her horse. As she rises above the Ocean, she greets the world with a wave of her hand. A dolphin is going before her, between the legs of the animal. Her presence is explained by the magical relationship that was supposed to exist between the moon and the fortunes of women, and also the disc of the mirror. The mirror from Eretria is dated to the end of the fifth century B.C.; it accompanied in the tomb a woman who had died prematurely.

Amongst the collection of folding mirrors, it is worth mentioning the scene on the cover of the mirror no. **7416** from Eretria, depicting Boreas and Oreithyia, and also the early mirror nos. **7670+7670a**, from Eretria, with a small double cover A) Dionysos and Ariadne, B) Eros on the knees of Aphrodite. As the diameter of the cover and the relief on it get bigger, the type spreads from the most important Mainland centres (Athens, Corinth, Chalkis) and reaches Ionia on the one hand, and Magna Graecia on the other, where specialist workshops came into being. The Corinthian preference was for the female head, as in the mirror no. **7424**. Even the provincial Mainland workshops did not remain indifferent, for there was a demand for folding mirrors there too. The cover of the folding mirror from Demetrias, in silver, is richer than usual. On the right, the young shepherd, Endymion, cowers in terror at the sudden appearance of Selene. She is depicted full length and dominates the centre of the cover; a Cupid moves towards the pair, holding a sword, and a dog is running away at the left.

On separate stands

Nos. **7914**, **7913**. *Funerary urns.* Along with the development of the repoussé art of the mirror covers, went a parallel change in the funerary urn. The attachment of the vertical handle ceases to be cast together with it, as it was in the urn no. **7914**, from Eretria, of Archaic type, where the Siren has been cast in one piece with the handle. In the other funerary hydria-urn, no. **7913**, also from Eretria, the handle was cast separately, and underneath it a relief repoussé metal plate has been attached. This new technique assisted the development of a two-figure scene; on the right a young Satyr is trying to "move" Dionysos — they are both merry-making. Although it was discovered at Eretria, the Attic nobility of the shape shows that it came from a workshop in Athens, and not, as has been supposed, in Chalkis. A statue of Praxiteles must have served as model for the figure of Dionysos.

No. 7913 Bronze hydria. From Eretria

On a separate stand

No. **7474:** Bronze statuette of an athlete from Sikyon, a work of the Polykleitan school. Second half of the fifth century B.C.

Case 27: The discovery from Ambelokipi

In 1969 workmen in the city of Athens were opening up a ditch for new water pipes not far from the Ambelokipi bus-stop, when they were surprised to see in the earth before them, at a depth of two metres, a number of bronze statues of different sizes. Since there is no indication at all that there was a workshop here, the most probable theory is that they were perhaps dedications in a sanctuary and they were hidden during the invasion of the Herulians in A.D. 267 or of the Goths at the end of the fourth century A.D.

Although the finds appear to be contemporary with one another, they are all very different. Some are copies on a smaller scale of Classical works, like the free copy of the discobolos of Myron, no. **16781**, and the Doryphoros of Polykleitos, or (on a separate column) the larger statue of a god (?) in the guise of a shepherd (no. **16789**).

No. **16787**. The statuette of a man juggling with balls belongs to a different period. He is wearing two crowns for symposia. One of the best Alexandrian works from the beginning of the second century B.C.

The statuette is at once interesting and problematic. The bronze-smith has logically followed through the contrasting turn of the Hellenistic period in the curious three-dimensional figure of a mime or similar character. The facial features are those of a foreign type, if not of a coloured slave, and the figure is difficult to understand outside the sphere of the theatre; it cannot be a new creation of the Roman period. Its eccentricity, and also the fact that it deviates from the flat form of the other figures, can only be explained in terms of its being a copy of an Alexandrian original of the second century B.C.

Fourth-century B.C. originals undoubtedly served as models for the bust of Sarapis with the μόδιον on his head, no. **16775**, and also for the statuette of Poseidon, who has his weight on his raised right leg; this last (no. **16772**) is a well known Lysippian type.

On a separate stand

No. **16789**. *Statue of Hermes (?) in the guise of a shepherd.* The bearded figure is dressed in a short chiton and holding a lamb. He stands on both feet on the broad base, and the right leg is slightly bent. The original must have been a noble work, the creation of one of the great bronze-sculptors of the Early Classical period, 460-450 B.C. – Myron or Kalamis, or some other, possibly from Aegina (?).

On separate stands

The largest statuettes of the discovery, nos. **16773-16774**, are clumsy and probably works of the Roman period, depicting Herakles-Dionysos etc.

No. 16789 Statue of Hermes (?) in the guise of a shepherd.
From Ambelokipi

119

PLAN OF THE 1ST FLOOR OF THE NATIONAL ARCHAEOLOGICAL MUSEUM

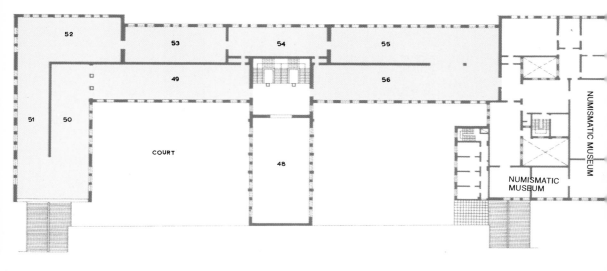

Vase collection

Vase Collection (Upper Floor)

ROOM 49 (Geometric vases)

The exhibition of vases from the Protogeometric and Geometric periods, in the first large room on this floor, forms an introduction to true Greek art, balance of the logos and the tectonic style.

The Geometric Style

When the unreasoning naturalistic art of Crete and Mycenae was succeeded by the poverty of that of the Late Mycenaean period, it was only the appearance of a new style that could save it from decay. The Geometric style, an expression of the rebirth of the world of the Greek mainland, constitutes a new application of the broad-lines of decoration found on Middle Helladic vases, clearly deployed with much greater reflection and a more vivid imagination. As early as the eleventh century, Athens was the centre and inspiration of the new style. Geometric art makes no use of flowers. This becomes clear if we compare the Geometric vases in this first room with the Palace Style amphoras on separate stands (from Kakovatos in Triphylia) at the entrance to it. The latter have bands of decoration showing plants and flowers, which have properly been recognised as indications of the cult of the great goddess of the animals and plants that remained alive until the end of the second millennium B.C. The Geometric style marks the appearance of a new religion, that of the Olympian deities, and behind the rational spirit governing it, there stands the figure of Apollo.

It was only after the end of the eighth century B.C., that a new style was to flourish initially with orientalising motifs; this was to co-

No 216 "Black Dipylon" style amphora

incide with a phenomenon of great historical importance, however, the invasion of art by myth, and more specifically by Greek myth.

This room, with very few exceptions, contains only Attic vases of the Geometric period and it is therefore possible to follow the aristocratic art of Athens, which now emerges for the first time as a metropolis.

The vase no. **18437** is still spherical in shape and decorated with wavy lines, though semicircles were to predominate throughout the eleventh century B.C.

In a case

No. **18042**. Small amphora. The semicircles are not yet incised with the compass.

On a separate stand

No. **815**. The meander makes a timid appearance. No. **219** has circles between the handles which are low down, as in the amphora no. **217**.

On separate stands

The three-footed base of the amphora no. **218** betrays Cypriote models.

The amphora no. **216** is the most sovereign expression of the "Black Dipylon" style (*SchwarzDipylon*). Eleventh century B.C. No. **18114**. Large decorated krater.

Case 2

Nos. **18102-18108**. Small oinochoai. No. **16363**. Fibulae. No. **16362**. Pins and no. **18112**. Clay doll.

Case 3

No. **18045**. Black amphora with a new motif on its neck: two small horses on either side of a swastika. Beginning of the ninth century B.C. The oinochoai are the outstanding pieces from the grave goods of a tomb in the region of the Areopagos; one, no. **15314**, has four "tiers" below the vase. No. **15318**. Pyxis with a modelled bucranium on the handle.

Case 4

A few dozen vases from the "Tomb of Isis" at Eleusis (the name is derived from the miniature figurine of the Egyptian goddess, no. **10963**). Pins and fibulae, also from the Early Geometric period.

No. 18020 Geometric cup with raised foliate motifs

Case 5

No. **18020**. Official footed cup, copied from a metal model. Ninth century B.C.

In a case

No. **802**. Large fragment of a krater in the classical Geometric style.

Case 13

Severe beautiful vases in the Early Geometric style, from the gift by Gregorios Empedokles. No. **18132**. Pyxis with three horses on the handle. Ninth century B.C. No. **18121**. Elegant "black" amphora. Ninth century B.C. No. **18425**. Attractive early small pyxis.

Case 6

Nos. **169, 186**. Vases from a tomb near the Pnyx. The bronze tripod no. **7940** is the work of a Cypriote bronze-smith. No. **152**. Small oinochoe, probably from the workshop of the Dipylon painter; *Circa*. 750 B.C. Two good examples of pyxides: the spherical no. **16347** and no. **197**, which is later. Two fine oinochoai of the eighth century B.C. On the neck of the oinochoe no. **17497** there is a scene probably depicting the magical invocation of the dead with (echoing?) vases etc. Middle of the eighth century B.C.

On a separate stand

Large oinochoe, no. **226**, with bands of rich decoration in which the meander triumphs. Second half of the eighth century. B.C. The black lustre begins to disappear.

Cases 7

Finds from tombs in Piraeus Street. Large fragments with excellent paintings of ships.

Case 8

No. **194**. Oinochoe with dancers (doing the *pyrrhichios*). No. **784**. Small cup (*kylix*), with a procession of women advancing towards the statue of a seated goddess.

Case 10

No. **874**. Deep cup, outstanding in its motif and technique. In the interior is a dance (*syrtos*) for men and women. The men's bodies are in silhouette, and the lower parts of the women's in outline. Second half of the eighth century B.C. No. **17457**. Oinochoe, with a lively fox-hunting scene on the shoulder. *Circa* 730 B.C.

Case 11 (on the wall)

This contains sherds from vases with incised letters. The name Nikodemos can be made out on one sherd. The simple oinochoe no. **192** is from the Dipylon. It was discovered in 1871, and has the famous inscription on the shoulder, proclaiming that it is the prize for whichever of the dancers danced best. It is still the earliest example of writing in Attica. Second half of the eighth century B.C. (the period of the *Iliad*).

On a separate stand

No. **17935**. Amphora, with a procession of hoplites carrying round shields (of "Argolic type") on the lower band.

Case 12

A profusion of geometric patterns. Two clay heads from the Amyklaion (Sparta): no. **4382** of the Late Mycenaean period, and no. **4381**, dated to the Geometric period by its vital face and wide-open eyes. No. **148**. Austere pyxis with a plastic horse on the lid. No. **17973**. With three horses, is later and less attractive.

No. 4181 Clay Geometric head. From the Amyklaion

No. 4382 Small clay Mycenaean head. From the Amyklaion

No. 14477 Kyathos

No. 18062 Amphora with a warrior procession

Case 14

Attic vases of the Late Geometric period, from tombs at Anavyssos in Attica. No. **14477**. Kyathos with a lively picture of a tumbler (acrobatic dancer). No. **14437**. Corinthian kotyle. No. **14475**. Small cup; two lions are preparing to tear a man apart. Second half of the eighth century B.C.

On stands

The monumental period of Geometric art is represented by the large funerary amphora no. **803**, a real achievement in pottery. It is slightly later than the one standing on the lower floor (Room 7) (no. **804**). The shape is long and thin, and is matched by the bodies painted on the vase. Between the handles a corpse is being taken for burial in a chariot, and there are male mourners on the left. There is a large procession of men below, and there are women (here dressed!) underneath the handles. A work of the Dipylon painter. *Circa* 740 B.C.

ROOM 50
(Geometric vases from different workshops)

On a separate stand

No. **18062**. Amphora. The warriors in the procession are carrying the Archaic octagonal "Boeotian" shield. Between the handles is a scene of the laying out of a dead man. Middle of the 8th century B.C. No. **16022**. Oinochoe with mourning women around the neck.

On separate stands

No. **810**. Attic krater with a high base. The scene of naked girls (slaves?) dancing to a lament, is unique. The horses, with their long necks, like the decoration, are typical of the decay of Geometric art. Copy of a large bronze cauldron. No. **990**. Large Geometric funerary krater from the Dipylon. Around and above the chariot bearing the corpse are men with swords and naked female mourners. A masterpiece by the Dipylon painter.

Case 20

Vases with a variety of shapes from Archaic Lakonian and Boeotian workshops. No. **234**. Part of a Lakonian vase from the Amyklaion at Sparta, depicting dancers at the festival of Apollo of Amyklai. The design on the Boeotian vases nos. **236** and **12896** is very rustic, while by contrast, that on the Argive vases nos. **230**, **213**, **877** and **843** is fine and accurately executed. No. **14481**. Clay four-wheeled cart from Euboea, loaded with amphoras of the seventh century B.C.

On a separate base

No. **220**. Boeotian amphora, with the unusual picture of the goddess Potnia, the Mistress of animals, birds and fish.

On the wall

No. **313**. The famous Attic hydria from Analatos. It is a very slen-

No. 990 Large Geometric funerary krater from the Dipylon

124

der and most expressive vase, recalling the beginning of the Orientalising style.

On a separate base

No. **17762**. Krater from the H. Schliemann Collection (donated by Antonios Benakis in 1943). The painting on the main side is valuable evidence for the early influence of myth in Attic art. An armed charioteer (Amphiaraos?) is in his chariot and a woman standing opposite him is holding a child. First half of the seventh century B.C.

Case 19

The Corinthian aryballos evolved from the spherical shape (the small aryballos no. **18648** is charming: cf. also the larger ones nos. **18625**, **18637** and **18544**) to the shape of the alabastron, nos. **18689** and **18741**. Corinthian kotyle with radiate decoration.

Case 21

Vases and clay figurines from Boeotian tombs. The "fruit-stands" (nos. **240-241**) on bases have paintings of flying birds (*Vogelschalen*) and plant decoration, typical of the Orientalising style which covers the sixth century, too, especially in Boeotian figurines. The clay figurines, or "Priests" (*Papades*), as the Boeotian villagers called them when they were discovered, are representative of Boeotian popular art and religion. Most of them have the schematic shape of effigies; their lower body is unformed and they continue without innovations. No. **5692**. Bell-shaped figurine. The bottom shelf of the case has figurines of horses. No. **12573**. Late Geometric oinochoe with a series of zones consisting of rather dull concentric circles.

Case (not numbered)

The best figurines are in the small case on the wall. Nos. **258-259**. Two large round vases. No. **13257**. Figurine of a goddess seated on an official throne. No. **4017**. Figurine of a horseman. No. **4010**. Figurine of a goddess with a *polos* on her head. No. **4009**. Good, slender figurine of a goddess. No. **12995**. Figurine of a dog with holes in its feet. No. **276**. Large pyxis with running dogs, probably of Euboean origin.

ROOM 51
Vases in the Orientalising style

On a separate stand

The large amphora no. **14497**, from Kynosarges in Athens, is a Cycladic shape vested with the Attic monumental size and colour. The decorations of the handles are *à jour*. On the neck are two wrestlers facing each other (Argonauts?). Their naked bodies are white. Of the belly, a charioteer and another male figure are preserved in a chariot with winged horses. On the left are the remains

No. 911 The earliest of the famous Melian amphoras

No. 313 Excellent hydria from Analatos. Early Attic art

No. 4017 Boeotian figurine of a horseman

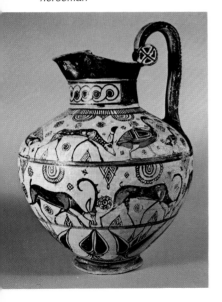

No. 12717 Rhodian oinochoe

of the body of a woman. Departure of the dead man for the Isles of the Blessed? Middle of the seventh century B.C.

On a separate stand

No. **11708**. Naxian amphora. The slip is yellow, and it has the long and narrow shape typical of Naxos. The neck is decorated with upright wild animals.

Cases 24-27

In addition to a selection of Cypriote vases, the Orientalising style in the islands is represented by two Rhodian oinochoai with bands of animals and a delicate shape (nos. **12717** and **12718**). No. **18801**. Small head, of wood, from Samos. No. **12509**. Small, expressive clay protome (sphinx) from a fine Cretan pithos. Seventh century B.C.

On separate stands

The earliest of the four much praised Melian amphoras (no. **911**) is decorated with a fantastic early myth: Apollo in a chariot at the moment of his epiphany, with two Hyperborean Maidens, and Artemis on the right; on the neck is the duel between Achilles and Memnon.

Case 28

The amphoras from Eretria are exhibited on a long separate stand. They are the work of local craftsmen. Below are vases from the Late Geometric period.

No. **12129** has the most striking painting in the series: a large sphinx, with a *polos* on its head. No. **12077**. The women carrying olive branches on the neck are named on the amphora. No. **12128**. Goddesses. Inscription: ΘΕΑΙ.

On a separate stand

The krater no. **801** is one of the earliest works of the Ram Jug painter and has a very rare shape. The sphinxes on the upper band are of early Archaic style, with sword-shaped wings, in outline. The band with silhouettes of deer that decorates the belly has the delicacy of its Cycladic models. Second quarter of the seventh century B.C.

Case 31

No. **4157**. Clay figurine of a female mourner, dressed in black. No. **993**. Proto-Attic krater; A. Swans. B. Climbing plants. No. **2226**. Inscribed fragment of a krater-skyphos from Aegina. The two letters ΑΛ are the beginning of the name Alexandros (Paris) or Agamemnon.

On separate stands

No. **221**. The "Siren amphora", the earliest Attic amphora without a neck, is probably an early work by the Nessos painter. *Circa* 630 B.C.

No. 1002 Brilliant amphora by the Nessos painter

Vases from Anagyrous. Domination of the black-figure style

Finds from a tumulus at Anagyrous in Attica. No. **16382**. Krater-skyphos with base. It is the earliest vase in the series, and is decorated only with wild animals and eagles (the slip is yellow). On the handle a deer is being torn apart by eagles. The belly of the slightly later krater, no. **16384**, has a scene of Prometheus bound and on the foot a procession of women carrying olive branches.

No. **16383**. Similar krater with a wonderfully lively scene of youths galloping headlong (in the first Panathenaia?). These three kraters are painted by the Nessos painter (formerly called the Chimaera painter).

Case 29

Nos. **16360**, **16357** and **16362**. Lekanai by the Panther painter, a pupil of the Nessos painter. *Circa* 610 B.C.

Case 34

A different, less powerful hand painted Herakles' contest with the Centaurs (krater-skyphos no. **16400**), which comes from the same find. No. **16285**. Black-figure oinochoe. Aristaios, the pre-Hellenic god of the etesian winds, is holding the pick-axe and the bag with the honey that he is about to give to mankind. By the Kerameikos painter. *Circa* 600 B.C.

On separate stands

No. **1003**. Amphora with (A-B) a bust of horses *en face* (*Pferdekopf* amphora), from Velanideza in Attica. It was used as a funerary urn to hold the bones of the dead man. No. **16388**. Large krater of Corinthian type, from the tomb at Anagyrous. Eagles tearing apart a snake. No. **1002**. The scene with which the Nessos painter decorated the neck is based on an ancient myth that was enacted at the river Euenos in Aetolia: Herakles is killing the Centaur Nessos. On the belly are two fearsome Gorgons, depicted without mercy, running to the right; behind them is the Medusa, beheaded by Perseus. The black-figure style and anthropomorphism have here started their brilliant course.

ROOM 52 (Finds from the Argive Heraion)

Attic black-figure vases from the 6th century

Case 46

The absence of monumental tombstones and funerary amphoras from the tombs of Attica is to be explained in terms of a known social phenomenon — the campaign of Solon against the insolence and pride of the aristocratic families (the Eupatrids).

The Gorgon painter (so called from an excellent lebes in the Louvre), the best painter in the early Attic black-figure style, was possibly a pupil of the Nessos painter. The wild animals retreat to the lower bands of decoration in most of the vases from this period. The collection possesses only fragments by the painter. Those ex-

No. 15165 Fragment of a Sophilos lebes. From the Acropolis

No. 15499 Fragment of a Sophilos lebes. From Pharsala

hibited in this case were discovered on the Acropolis and were without doubt dedications to Athena Ergane. The fragments of the base of a krater of Anagyrous type, but later, with sphinxes and Sirens, has a charming air, deriving from the slip (an invention in the Gorgon painter's workshop) which adds lustre to the Attic clay. There are frequent incisions, and the faces of the animals are very merry. The same painter produced one of the earliest Attic plates with animals.

Sophilos, the first man in Attica to sign his work, was to depict legends unconnected with wild animals, with a charm previously unknown. The scene on the lebes no. **15165**, dedicated to Athena, reflects some unknown official Attic painting. The wedding of Peleus and Thetis is the subject of the main band. "Sophilos painted (lit. wrote) me" can be seen behind the palace door. Achilles, the son of Peleus and Thetis, is Sophilos' favourite hero.

No. **15499**. Large fragment of a lebes discovered at Pharsala, near Phthia, the home of the hero Achilles. It depicts the funeral games for Patroklos. Spectators, amongst whom is Achilles, are sitting on a wooden *exedra* and following the horse-races. Signature: "Sophilos wrote me", "Sophilos made me". *Circa* 580 B.C. No. **18002**. Fragment of a very delicate kantharos. Medusa is holding out her hands in supplication to Hermes.

The "reveller vases" in the same case are mainly the work of two painters inspired by Corinthian models. No. **640**. Kotyle, one of the finest Attic imitations of Corinthian models (group of revellers). The kotylai nos. **528** and **940** (group of revellers) are by the same painter.

Case 47

This case contains a number of later vases by Sophilos. No. **12587**. Krater of Corinthian type with a dynamic painting of Herakles wrestling with Nereus, the old man of the sea. Somewhat later, Sophilos' drawing becomes freer, without losing its charm. No. **991**. Loutrophoros with bands of animals. No. **995**. Small kalyx vase of Chian type, one of Sophilos' latest works.

No. **441**. Corinthian style krater from Boeotia.

No. **17984**. Early cup, one of the earliest from Attica; an imitation of Corinthian models. No. **18717**. Plate by the Polos painter, one of the less careful of this period. No. **11734**. Charming small vases with birds (four on a separate stand). No. **12688**. Three-footed cup showing a group of revellers. Band of revellers on the shoulder; there are also paintings on the flat feet.

On a separate stand

No. **1036**. Amphora from the tumulus of the Marathonomachoi (Marathon fighters), late work of Sophilos. It has a large number of bands of animals and the free drawing is combined with a wealth of descriptive detail: Hermes, Artemis mistress of the animals.

Case 48

Some Boeotian works. No. **4082**. Clay *quadriga* with a charioteer and warrior. No. **12218**. Small askos with the signature of the potter Mnasalkes.

Nos. **4021-4030**. Small clay "spoons" with heads of animals in plastic elevation, most of them also having drawings. No. **12307**.

Nos. 4021-4030 Small clay spoons

Three-footed pyxis. On one of the feet, Aristaios, the god of the winds, is running with his bag in his hand. No. **16455**. Clay figurine of an ithyphallic daemon.

Case 35-37

A large part of this room is devoted to dedications found in the ancient sanctuaries, the Heraion of Argos and that of Perachora, the sanctuary of Artemis Orthia at Sparta, and the sanctuary at Thermon in Aetolia. Though they are mainly fragmentary, they are the finest exhibits in the room. The large case on the right contains finds from the Argive Heraion: vases and figurines of the Mycenaean period. The large pyxis no. **14199**, from the end of the Geometric period, has fine plant decoration. The Corinthian oinochoai no. **14175**, with high necks, are from the late Geometric period; they are decorated with finely drawn bands. No. **14180**. Large Corinthian kotyle with fine radiating lines. No. **16554**. Bronze statuette from Egypt.

Case 39

Clay and bronze dedications, many of them of excellent quality, though damaged, and all of them from the Argive Heraion. Nos. **14037** and **14039**. Bronze pins of early style. No. **13971**. Large neck and head of a swan, in bronze, from a lebes. End of the seventh century B.C. No. **16357**. Torso of a *kouros*, a solid Doric work by an Argean bronze-smith.

Nos. **14210** and **14214**. Two clay plaques with the figure of Aristaios. A large number of small heads from clay figurines dating to the sixth and fifth centuries B.C.

Case 40

The triangular case against the wall contains the famous bronze metal plaque (once applied to a larnax?), from the hand of an Argean repoussé worker. No. **15131**. The murder of Kassandra by Klytemnestra. *Circa* 600 B.C.

From the two sanctuaries at Perachora (those of Hera Limenia and Hera Akraia) comes no. **16519**. Fine ivory Sphinx; seventh century B.C. Small head, no. **16520** and small reliefs, nos. **16522**, **16524**, also in ivory, with eastern workmanship. No. **16510**. Clay figurine of a daemon, of Corinthian craftsmanship. The small clay square temple no. **15471** (on a separate stand), from the Argive Heraion, was a dedication to Hera. The projecting pediment is supported by two columns. *Circa* 680 B.C. An earlier type of temple is reflected in the other small clay temple, no. **16684**, from Perachora (on a separate stand); it has an apse at the rear and dates from the Geometric period.

Case 43

Nos. **16160-16161**. Small Geometric horses. No. **16173**. Bronze dove, a wonderful piece of work from the seventh century B.C. No. **16152**. Statuette of Zeus throwing the thunderbolt; a Corinthian work *Circa* 450 B.C. No. **16156**. Small bronze ox, with the inscription: "Naumachos dedicated me to Hera Limenia". Second half of the sixth century. B.C. No. **16146**. Bronze karyatid mirror; Corinthian work. End of the sixth century B.C.

No. 15471 Clay square temple, dedicated in the Heraion at Argos

Case 49

A variety of dedications: vases, clay figurines etc., Protocorinthian oinochoai, fragments of exquisite Protocorinthian vases (animals, sphinxes). No. **16503**. Small clay *kouros*, Corinthian work. Plastic vases: No. **16592**. Siren. No. **16517**. Sandals, Rhodian work. Large number of small heads from clay figurines coming from a variety of workshops — Argive, Corinthian, Ionian. Ivory seals. No. **16447**. Clay plaque, Aristaios. Early red-figure vase (mastos-kotyle: no. **19575**) A. Broadly drawn Siren. B. Sphinx. *Circa* 520 B.C.

On a separate stand

No. **17870**. Body of a clay sphinx; an akroterion from the temple at Kalydon. One of the best Corinthian works of its kind.

The clay metopes and roof-tiles from the third temple at Thermon in Aetolia afford valuable evidence for the architectural members of an Archaic temple. They are the works of Corinthian artists who made their contribution to the development of the Doric style. The figures on the metopes are enshrouded by a sense of distant mystery. *Circa* 630 B.C. They are displayed on the wall of the narrow, south side of Room 52.

Case 41

Corinthian vases. No. **625**. Mastos with revellers. A small number of plastic vases: hares (nos. **3929**, **10778**), and a lovely panther no. **3903**.

No. **16289**. Small alabastron with Gorgons.

No. **333**. Large aryballos with Boreades. No. **536**. Phiale with obscene ritual dances. The small amphora no. **664** has a charming picture of the lame Hephaistos being accompanied to Olympos; a god with a vine-branch (Dionysos?).

Case 42

Corinthian vases in a variety of shapes. No. **18668**. Large alabastron with Boreades. No. **281**. Aryballos with a ship, oarsmen, boatswain and captain. The oinochoai nos. **262** and **263**, with bands of animals, are precisely drawn. The freshness of the narrative in Corinthian painting may be seen in the subject of the simple small vase no. **277**. Achilles is waiting for Troilos and Polyxene is at the spring with a hydria. At the side is Priam. Inscription: "Timonidas wrote me". *Circa* 580 B.C.

Central table

The wooden plaques from Pitsa are the only remains we have of Corinthian miniature painting. One, and part of another, are better preserved than the rest. The material is wood, with a white slip on it, and the figures are in tempera. The first, no. **16464**, has a lamb being taken for sacrifice on the altar. The other plaque, no. **16465**, is slightly later, as may be seen from the very skilful composition of the figures: on the right are three women, two of them in the foreground, and the middle on a secondary plane, and behind, to the left, are the faces of women facing each other. The hair of all the figures is blond, the outline rose-coloured, the himatia are red and white and the peploi blue. Even without the inscriptions, we would call these

No. 17870 Body of a clay sphinx. From Kalydon

Clay metope from Thermos in Aetolia

133

delightful figures Nymphs. The sacrificial procession on the first plaque is moving towards them. *Circa* 540 B.C. The second is about 500 B.C.

Case 50

From the sanctuary of Artemis Orthia at Sparta. A large number of dedications, both small and large, of ivory or bone; most of them are local works. Square plaques with relief figures and a bronze fibula fastened to the rear surface. No. **15511**. Couple facing each other. Probably a work of eastern art. Nos. **15332-15334**. Figurines of women, made of bone. The most impressive of all the ivory works is the largest, semicircular relief, no. **15362**. Large ivory plaque: warship with rowers, warriors carrying shields etc. On the left, a woman is saying farewell to the captain. Mythical? No. **15368**. Comb; the judgement of Paris. The three goddesses are walking towards Paris, who is sitting on a throne (he is not holding an apple in his hand). Nos. **15338**, **15329**, **15331**, **15339**. Female busts, made of bone.

Case 44

No. **15616**. Figurine of a seated animal with winged Aristaios on the reverse. No. **15917**. Plaque with relief Gorgon. No. **15631**. Seals: trapezoid plaques with female head in relief. No. **15630**. Relief female head. No. **15366**. Male head facing left with outline *à jour*. Nos. **15664**, **15626-15628**. Similar, earlier seals. No. **15495**. Ivory figurine; two females on a formal throne.

ROOM 53
(Black-figure vases of the sixth century B.C.)

Case 51

A selection of vases from the excavations of the cemetery at Anagyrous (Vari) in Attica. The larger vases, especially the hydrias, have clumsy shapes. They are nearly all charred by the funeral pyres.

No. **19176**. Oinochoe with an ox and a lion facing each other; powerful work by the Gorgon painter.

No. **19159**. Oinochoe with Hermes and Sphinxes. No. **19174**. Kantharos with a chariot painted *en face*. No. **19171**. Fine early plate with Gorgon. No. **19167**. Lekythos with a yellow glaze, by the Edinburgh painter: hunters. No. **19163**. Lekythos with an archaic shape, by the Amasis painter.

On a separate stand

A unique four-wheel funeral chariot in clay, from a tomb at Anagyrous. The death bed is on a table, covered with a long cloth; another cloth, under which there is a small clay figurine, covers the

No. 19159 Black-figure oinochoe with Hermes and Sphinxes

No. 16465 Wooden votive tablet representing a sacrificial scene. From the Pitsa cave, Corinthia

Unique clay four-wheeled chariot from the Anagyrous cemetery

No. 606 Large lebes (dinos) with black-figure representations. From the Acropolis

No. 529 The Ross kylix

No. 529 Interior of the Ross kylix

body of the dead man. The charioteer goes in front and there are mourning women at the sides.

Case 52

Small finds from the sanctuaries of Poseidon and Athena at Sounion. No. **14930**. Small lead *kouros* from the sixth century B.C. Small bronze and iron dedications. Fragments of black-figure votive plaques. The painting on the Attic plaque no. **14935** is unusual. Warship; five hoplites with helmets and round shields; in the stern the boatswain is holding a large rudder. Work of the Analatos painter (cf. the hydria no. **313** in Room 50). Beginning of the seventh century B.C.

Finds from Skillous near Olympia. No. **11120**. A small clay temple, is the most important of them. Nos. **12680** and **13910**. Lakonian kylikes with the usual floral decoration outside. Inside, on the left, is the bust of a man, on a yellow ground. He is wearing a purple band around his hair and a himation, and he has a long beard. 540 B.C.

Case 59

No. **18880**. Large plate by the painter Lydos, from the Acropolis. Herakles fighting with Kyknos. No. **507**. Smaller plate by the same painter. Achilles receiving his panoply from Thetis in his homeland Phthia. *Circa* 550 B.C.

Black-figure lekythoi of the sixth century B.C., with archaic shapes – a broad shoulder, or the alabastron shape ("Deianeira type"). No. **567**. Without a shoulder: Dionysos and a Satyr. No. **413**. Zeus, seated in the centre, receives Herakles on Olympos. No. **414**. Slightly later: the arming of a warrior. No. **524**. Herakles and a Triton.

On a separate stand

The wonderful large lebes (dinos) from the Acropolis, no. **606**, from which comes the name "The 606 Painter". This masterpiece of ceramic art is one of the two or three to survive intact out of the great number of vases dedicated on the Acropolis to Athena Ergane by artists and vase-painters. The broadest of the bands encircling the body depicts a many-figured epic battle; it is of the Homeric period and not contemporary with the vase-painter, since the struggle of the two sides for the corpse of the dead warrior involves the use of chariots (the phalanx now predominated in warfare). *Circa* 560 B.C.

Case 60

No. **559**. The "amphora of Olympos", probably a "proto-Panathenaic" vase (before 566 B.C.). A. One of the two figures wearing himatia and listening to the flute-player is excellent (the mythical Olympos?), as is the bird raising its neck. B. Youth on horseback and a groom.

The artists of the Kerameikos in Athens imitated Corinthian cups from 600 B.C. onwards, though they developed and ennobled the shape over two whole centuries. No. **533**. This early Attic cup still has a low base. No. **531**. Cup. Duel. No. **529**. The "Ross kylix" (named after its initial publication by the German archaeologist Ross) is one of the finest from its period. In the interior are Herakles and the Centaur Nessos. "Very close to the Heidelberg painter" (Beazley). Corinthian oinochoai from Tegea and cups. No. **521**. Oinochoe, of local Corinthian shape. No. **992**. The "Sofouliscup" took its name from the archaeologist and politician who first published it. No. **641**. Another Corinthian cup. No. **330**. A similar one with a Gorgoneion in the centre.

Case 57

Beautiful Attic vases, most of them from about 560 B.C. The most important ones are cups. No. **493**. Early lekythos with an unusual shape, depicting women seated before an altar. From the workshop of a skilled potter ("affecter"). No. **435**. Cup of "Siana" type, by the Heidelberg painter. The cups nos. **12709**, **12668** and **12667** are from the same hand. No. **1055**. Round aryballos with a Gorgoneion incised on the flat surface of the handle. The dedicatory inscription on the rim (to Phokis gave [me]) also mentions the name of Mnesikleides and (the painter) Kealtes. No. **14907**. Very delicate cup without a base. No. **12552**. Cup. At the edges are two people drinking on a couch.

No. 17873 Cup of old style

On a separate stand

No. **3886**. Stone stele of a warrior; discovered at Kaminia on Lemnos in 1886. A warrior carrying a spear, engraved in light relief. The two inscriptions on the main surface and the side remain undeciphered. The alphabet is probably a local one.

Case 53. Finds from Lemnos

Nos. **19264-5**. Two small houses and fountains with three partitions. No. **19259**. Clay figurine of a goddess. No. **19248**. Base of a vase showing Artemis, the fierce mistress of the animals. Nos. **19230-1**. Large clay plaques with Sirens.

Case 61

Altar with fragments from the Acropolis.

Case 58

Ionian vases and clay figurines. No. **14625**. Rhodian amphora of the Fikellura type with large-scale plant decoration. Nos. **5669** and **5397**. Clay figurines (plastic vases) of *korai,* of Samian type. No. **2072** etc. Delicate plastic vases in the shape of sandals, and Boeotian imitations.

Case 62

Band cups. In contrast with the calyx type, which have the rim in the ground colour, the subject on the panelled ones is between the handles, and the rest of the body is black. These cups are severe, silent and rhythmical. One variation involves bands of decoration below the level of the handles ("Droop cups"). No. **17873**. Fine early cup. A. Busts of a woman and two men. B. Similar one with female heads; the names are given: Kalitine, Simules.

Nos. **9711**, **12281** and **12708**. Severe; duellers and other figures. No. **661**. Droop cup. Battles. A variety of colour. No. **363**. Arming of a warrior. Fine art. No. **433**. Skyphos. Aias is supporting the body of Achilles on his back. No. **18870**. Amphora with decoration of me-

Kalyx krater from Pharsala

137

No. 1004 Large wedding lebes. From Eretria

topes. A. Horseman, inscription "Anthippos". B. A similar one. No. **1007**. Amphora from Eretria with dull glaze. A. Two warriors. B. Satyr mounting an animal. No. **151111**. Amphora by the Swing painter. A. Two men carrying clubs.

On a separate stand

Calyx krater from Pharsalos. A. Battle above and in front of the body of Patroklos. B. Similar scene *en face*. There are vine shoots on the sides. A free, rather poor copy of the excellent krater in the Agora Museum, the work of Exekias, found on the Acropolis. The National Museum krater was probably from his workshop. *Circa* 530 B.C.

Case 55

Two clay sarcophagi from Klazomenai. No. **13939** is the earlier and has three animals with deer and lions below them. No. **13472** is black-figure, with rough chariots. There is a fine fragment in the case with Klazomenian vases and sherds: no. **5610** with two gods on a throne and worshippers (the men's faces are also white).

On a long stand

Three black-figure wedding lebetes from Eretria. The earliest, no. **12076**, has unskilled drawing but lively colours. Wedding. *Circa* 550 B.C. No. **1004**. The most official – the wedding of Peleus and Thetis. Remains of the names. No. **12075**. Herakles and the Lernian Hydra.

Case 63

Fragments of black-figure plaques with funerary subjects. They were probably applied to funerary monuments. Nos. **2414-2417**. From the hand of Exekias. Remains of an inscription (Ch)arita. No. **12697**. The laying out of the dead. Mourners. B. Men raising their hands. Nos. **2410**, **2412** and **2413**. Large plaque. Men in a funeral procession. Inscription: "This is the tomb of Areias". *Circa* 530 B.C. The black-figure lekythoi in this case have a shape that has almost taken its final form. The shape of the lekythos no. **12776** is Late Archaic: it depicts Dionysos seated with a rhyton in his hand. No. **18566**. A Centaur fighting with a Lapith. By the Athens painter. So is no. **514**. Poseidon riding a sea-horse with a dolphin behind him. The same painter also produced the lekythos no. **513** with the superb picture of the Sun setting in his chariot; on the left Herakles, on a rock, is greeting the rising of the Sun. *Circa* 490 B.C.

ROOM 54 (Black-figure and red-figure vases)

Case 65

Black-figure lekythoi from the beginning of the fifth century B.C., with a yellow glaze and mythological subjects. The best of them are amongst the latest works of the Athena painter. There are rare subjects on the lekythoi by the Beldam painter. No. **1138**. The vase from which the painter took his name, Athena, seated. No. **1132**. Herakles supporting the arch of heaven, while Atlas brings him the apples of the Hesperides. No. **1133**. By the Athena painter. Circe transforming the companions of Odysseus into swine. No. **18567**. Satyrs dancing the *pyrrhichios* to the accompaniment of the flute. It is the best work by this painter. No. **19296**. Fine amphora with Apollo. Nos. **555-557**. Black-figure oinochoai from Kameiros on Rhodes.

Case 64

No. **1129**. Lekythos by the Beldam painter. Torture, the punishment of an Arabess, Lamia or Beldam, by Satyrs. No. **487**. Punishment of pirates (?) on a boat.

Case 73

Boeotian and Attic works. No. **4431**. Clay disc with clay figurines of women making bread and an oven. Delightful work of popular art, as is the one like it, no. **5773**. They were found in tombs. No. **4569**. Boeotian figurine of a maiden holding a locust. No. **5708**. Clay figurine of a man playing the kithara. Boeotian black-figure vases; the black silhouettes without incision are a reminiscence of the Geometric period.

Case 74

No. **398**. Attic lekythos. The wrestling match between Peleus and Thetis. No. **12767**. Alabastron with a yellow glaze. The dogs of Artemis tearing apart Aktaion. No. **16350**. Lekythos. Herakles killing the sleeping giant Halkyoneus. The young winged Sleep is sitting on the body of the latter. By the Beldam painter; so is no. **599**. The daughter of King Pelias, the lebes with the ram in the centre. No. **18633**. Similar subject. No. **548**. Three women race towards an altar.

Black-figure lekythoi of the early fifth century B.C. are of interest for their mythological scenes but of mediocre execution.

Case 75

Lekythoi by the Edinburgh painter. No. **1124**. The shape is still heavy. Theseus and the bull. *Circa* 500 B.C. No. **1130** is later. Odysseus tied to the mast and Sirens. No. **550**. Charming motif depicting Peleus bringing Achilles to his tutor, the Centaur Cheiron. No. **14459**. Amphora, by the same painter. A. An Amazon carrying a dead Amazon on her back.

Case 67

Vase from the women's quarter. No. **2184**. Epinetron. At the front is a plastic bust of a goddess, and there are black-figure paintings on the sides. Amazons. By the Sappho painter, like the three following lekythoi, with delicate drawings. No. **2262**. Minotaur (Six technique). No. **552**. Polyxene at the spring and Achilles. No. **595**. Chariot, with an altar in the foreground.

Case 66

Skyphoi by the Theseus painter, and the painter of the group with the white heron or the saffron (the latter name comes from the

No. 550 Black-figure lekythos. Peleus, Achilles and Cheiron

139

No. 735 Kalyx krater

No. 2385 Plastic vase, head of an Ethiopian

No. 2061 Plastic vase, head of a Maenad?

colour of the dress). No. **635**. Skyphos, with Herakles playing the *kithara*. No. **12531**. Skyphos, with a picture of a fountain. No. **18720**. Skyphos. The Sphinx of Thebes, on a column capital, rushing forward. In front a seated man wearing the himation. No. **1153**. Small loutrophoros. No. **447**. Panathenaic amphora.

Case 76

Table with fragments of vases from the Acropolis (late black-figure and early red-figure).

On separate stands

No. **1361**. Red-figure calyx krater from the Acropolis. Maenad and Satyr. No. **735**. Calyx krater by the Syriskos painter. Theseus and the Minotaur, Ariadne and the other figures. From the Acropolis. *Circa* 460 B.C.

Case 70

Fragments of vases from the Acropolis, works by the best painters. The majesty of the large amphoras by the Kleophrades painter (Epiktetos 2nd), and by the Pan painter can be seen in the remains showing scenes of the Battle of the Giants and other subjects. A good number of fragments of cups from Makron, including the enchanting cup with a scene of the small Dionysos being handed over to the Nymphs by Zeus. The signature of the potter is incised on the handle: "Hieron made [me]". Fragments of superb vases from the hand of the dazzling Brygos painter. Neck of a loutrophoros by Phintias. *Circa* 490 B.C.

Case 77

A variety of red-figure vases from different provenances. Plastic vases (aryballoi): nos. **2385** and **11725**, in the shape of the head of an Ethiopian. The black glaze was precisely what was needed to render the black skin. No. **2385** is from Eretria. The name "Leagros the fair" is incised on the rim. Three of the most graceful early alabastra. No. **1740**. By Paseas ("Cerberos painter"). No. **1239**. Young man visiting a *hetaira*. No. **15002**. From Delphi, with a white slip. Maenad and Amazon. Signature "Pasiades made [me]". No. **1357**. Cup with a man at a banquet singing as he reclines on his couch. No. **1628** signed: "Phintias made [me]". No. **1409**. Fine larger cup with the potter's signature: "Panphaios made [me]". No. **1425**. A young man (at a symposium) bends towards a basin. The simple turn of the emblem is indicative of an early date for these kylikes, before the circle with maeander held sway. *Circa* 500 B.C. In the fine pelike no. **1413**, the lively picture of a mature man offering a hare as a love token to a handsome youth. *Circa* 500 B.C. Pelike with an amusing woman at the fountain. Akin to the Nikoxenos painter. *Circa* 490 B.C. No. **1482**. Hydria. The Centaur Pholos (the front part of the body is human) returning from hunting. By the Eucharides painter. *Circa* 490 B.C.

Case 71

Red-figure vases. Nos. **422, 423, 481, 412, 13887**. White alabastra with Ethiopians. In nos. **422** and **423** thee figures are wearing eastern trousers. Plastic vases with heads. No. **2061** has a very sweet female face. No. **18570**. White alabastron with a scene of a palaestra. Two naked youths on the verge of adolescence and a cock. Inscription: "Phanos the fair". No. **1666**. The "Trikoupis cup", presented by the great politician. "Athenodotos the fair" on the background round the emblem. A.B. Two of the labours of Theseus and again "Athenodotos the fair" on one of the exterior surfaces. *Circa* 490 B.C. No. **15375**. Aryballos-shaped lekythos with the signature of the potter Douris: "Douris made [me]", and the dedicatory inscription: "The lekythos [is for] Asopodoros". It has a picture of fairytale beauty: two Erotes are pursuing a youth. From the hand of Douris; an excellent work of his middle period. *Circa* 480 B.C.

Case 72

Corinthian clay figurines: *korai*, Sirens and Gorgons. Late Archaic, beginning of the eighth century B.C.

Case 78

Mainly red-figure lekythoi, a good number of them from the hand of the Bowdoin painter. No. **17281**. Charming picture of a young athlete with stone jumping-weights of the Archaic type. No. **1272**. Artemis running towards an altar. Nos. **1621**, **1508**, **17295**, **17291**. The flying Nike is a familiar motif and reveals no imagination. The line of the painter is bright and willowy, however. No. **16346**. Small pelike. A. Pluto holding a large cornucopia. Demeter opposite him. No. **12394**. Larger lekythos with a reveller. Early, small work by the great Berlin painter. No. **1632**. Lekythos. Superb figure of a youth. *Circa* 460 B.C. Nos. **1305**, **1633** and **12803**. Three smaller lekythoi from Eretria, with the name Douris. They are thought to be by the Cartellino painter. *Circa* 470 B.C. No. **12782**. Amazon dressed in trousers and blowing a trumpet. By the Klügman painter, like no. **12780** (Amazon), nos. **11736**, **1311**, **1312** and perhaps also no. **1302** (Amazon).

On a separate stand

No. **18543**. Large amphora, with a broad rim. A. Theseus. B. The bull of Marathon. Work by the Syleus painter, one of the best exponents of the Severe Style. *Circa* 470 B.C.

ROOM 55
(The white lekythoi, "the flowers of death")

The National Museum's collection of white lekythoi, which is unique, is an expression of Classical vase-painting in Athens; it is to be interpreted in terms of funeral customs, and also of the move towards Classical art. Many of the finest white lekythoi were discovered in tombs in Eretria, where they were placed next to the deceased, as in Athens. Fragments of white lekythoi are also found in Athenian tombs, where they were sometimes thrown in order to break them in the funeral pyre.

Few vase-painters specialised in the decoration of white lekythoi from 470 or 460 B.C. onwards; the shape, and less frequently, the subject, was prepared by older vase-painters.

Later, from about 450 B.C., the milky white glaze combines with

No. 1827 Early lekythos with white Nike

the mobility of the line and the other-worldly meaning of the subjects to endow the Attic white-figure lekythoi with the much praised incorporeal sense of death.

Case 79

Lekythoi of a phase transitional to the new style. No. **1809**. Eros flying and pouring a libation (for the dead?), by the Athens painter. No. **1973**. Hunter, by the Bowdoin painter. The same also produced: no. **1964**, a hoplite. No. **1827**. Nike. No. **12588**. Maenad. No. **1792** and others with the painting in outline.

Case 88

Red-figure lekythoi with anthemia on the shoulders. No. **12801**. Lekythos by the Beldam painter. Early representation of a funeral stele. No. **17612**. Red-figure lekythion. An actor running wearing buskins. No. **16351**. Fragmentary red-figure hydria of archaic type (*kalpis*). Hermes and the deceased.

On a separate stand

No. **9683**. The famous pelike by the Pan painter, one of the best "mannerists" of the late Archaic period. *Circa* 480 B.C. Herakles defeating the Egyptian king Bousiris and his servants. Ethiopians are standing next to the fine altar, with implements for the sacrifice, spits, etc.

Case 80

No. **15190**. Attic white kylix from the Acropolis, the finest of all. A Thracian woman is preparing to raise an axe against Orpheus. Traces of the inscription: "Euphronios made [me]. Glaukon the fair". The outlines are in brilliant gold lines, and the faces have a divine beauty. *Circa* 460 B.C., from the hand of the Pistoxenos painter. Euphronios was the potter. He also produced the red-figure bobbin-shaped pot no. **2192**. A. Herakles and Nereus. B. Peleus and Thetis. No. **2350**. A similar, white vase with the chariot of Dawn (Eos) in the central circle, by a different painter. Around it is the rape of the daughters of Leukippos. B. Europa on a bull in the centre, surrounded by young men and women. No. **1237**. Kylix. A. Dionysos and a Satyr. B. Satyr and Maenad. By the painter 1237. No. **1240**. Fine red-figure alabastron. No. **2188**. Large white pyxis. Scene of the women's quarters. No. **1486**. Hydria by the Niobid painter. The oinochoe no. **14503** is more typical of this painter's work. A warrior pouring a libation, with broadleaved anthemia in the background. No. **1261**. Hydria, by a related painter. Youth pouring a libation. No. **1687**. Small fine pelike by the Nausikaa painter. No. **12461**. Cup with sporting scenes, all showing the vigour of the Penthesileia painter. The cup no. **17921** is also from his workshop. Conventional figures of young men. No. **15880**. Rhyton with a plastic head of a lamb. Figures on the neck in red-figure work; from the hand of the Villa Giulia painter. *Circa* 450 B.C. No. **12890**. Red-figure lekythos. Slender woman with a reflective face, holding a folded himation; by the Providence painter. No. **16457**. White alabastron with three women, one of them playing castanets. No. **4003**. Attic clay figurine of a reclining *hetaira*.

No. 2192 Red-figure "bobbin" pot

No. 9683 Red-figure pelike by the Pan painter

Case 89

No. **15112**. Column krater of Corinthian type. Goat with Dionysos and Satyrs. No. **1336**. Pelike; A. Zeus. B. Nike. The painting has no frame. No. **19352** is similar but has a frame. Both by the Naples painter. No. **1708**. Beautiful pyxis. Poseidon and Amphitrite, the Triton proposing marriage to a young woman. Amusing work by the Amphitrite painter. No. **17170**. Fine pelike, Hermaic stele, a youth with a lyre, and an altar. No. **19568**. Krater of Corinthian type. Herakles, Bousiris and his followers. No. **17532**. Large red-figure lekythos. Tall woman and a youth. Badly written "Kalos" (fair) (perhaps Alkimachos). No. **1416**. Pelike. A. Zeus and Ganymede. B. Zeus and Hera. No. **16277**. Small alabastron with fine figures towards the top.

On a separate stand

No. **1170**. Large official funeral loutrophoros from Pikrodafphni, Palaion Phaleron. On the belly is a maiden on her death-bed, her mother and a mourning Thracian woman (red hair). Cavalcade and men on foot, and there are mourning women on the neck. By the Painter of Bologna 228. It has been suggested that the figures of the women with their pent-up grief reflect Trojan women from the "Sack of Troy" by the painter Polygnotos in the Stoa Poikile at Athens.

Case 81

Large, early white lekythoi. This form was given elevation by the Achilles painter, and its female figures are large and severe, with character. The glaze is yellowish and extends onto the shoulder; the exposed parts of the women's bodies have an applied white colour. No. **1963** is one of the best. Woman and servant girl. Inscription: "Diphilos the fair, son of Melanopos". Dromippos the fair, son of Dromokleides is praised in the inscription on the lekythos no. **12744**, and Diphilos in most of the early ones by the Achilles painter. Nos. **1922**, **1923**, **13750**, **12441** etc. The top of no. **1963**, with the two large female figures, is exhibited next to it. The contemporary lekythoi nos. **1987**, **12770** and **12771** are from the hand of the Timokrates painter. The last has a unique picture of a small child on the shoulder of a servant girl. Inscription: "Alkimachos the fair".

Case 82

"Melian" clay reliefs, most of them *à jour*; The subjects are from myth. No. **15878**. The murder of Aktaion by the dogs of Artemis. No. **9753**. The recognition of Odysseus. No. **4195**. The sphinx has knocked a naked man to the ground. No. **4119**. Phrixos clinging to the ram. No. **16023**. Small red-figure pelike. A. Phrixos on the ram. By the Phrixos painter.

Case 83

No. **1426**. Amphora with twisted handles. No. **1298**. Red-figure lekythos (there is an offering on the funerary stele). The same painter produced the following three ones. No. **1299**. Young man and a simple stele. No. **1636**. Similar larger one. Stele with anthemion, a woman and a man. No. **1650**. Aryballos-shaped lekythos by the same man. Women's quarters. No. **12892**. Red-figure lekythos. No.

No. 12771 White lekythos

143

17495. Skyphos by the Penelope painter. A. Lover with dark gaze. B. Youth, somewhat startled. *Circa* 440 B.C.

Case 90

Different types of pyxides with a high base. Nos. **12904**, **11363** (with traces of painting), nos. **13918**, **11368**, **11362**. Various kinds of pyxides with superb workmanship. Marble "eggs" from tombs. Nos. **11377**, **12808** and the delightful miniature no. **11378**.

No. **1241**. Red-figure pyxis. Apollo, seated, and eight Muses, two are holding flutes, one a lyre and another a *kithara*; a Muse is standing in front of them holding an open cylinder. Fine work. *Circa* 450 B.C. It was discovered in a tomb in Athens outside the Kerameikos. Contents of an Athenian tomb: No. **15127**. Bronze mirror with Siren. No. **15128**. Similar one of the simple Corinthian type. No. **15303**. Alabaster pyxis. Nos. **15304-5**. Two small simple ones. No. **3864**. Shell from a tomb.

Case 84

Three white lekythoi. The most official is no. **1935**. Grave stele at the top of a staircase and a funeral mound behind. A god-like youth (the dead man) and a woman with a basket. By the Bosanquet painter.

No. **1818**. A woman and a young warrior. By the Achilles painter. No. **17916**. Use of many colours, with black for the outlines. Charon in his boat, Hermes and a dead woman. By the Charon painter (or Sabourof painter).

Case 85

White lekythoi from the advanced period of the Achilles painter. The dominant motif has two women face to face. The painter continues to insist on glaze outlines. but begins to add a grave stele between the figures; cf. no. **12791**, and the exceptionally fine no. **12784**; nos. **12745**, **1821**, **1823** and the red-figure no. **1639** are by the same man. The way the eyes of the two figures meet is full of the feeling of death. Nos. **1761** and **12792**. Lekythoi by the Thanatos painter; the latter shows the blonde dead woman wrapped in a purple himation.

Case 86

White lekythoi with matt outlines. No. **1814**. A mother taking her frightened child to Charon. No. **1954**. Large lekythos, by the Quadrate painter. No. **12783** is by the same man. Sleep, Death and Hermes the escorter of souls. No. **1926** is by the Charon painter (Charon in the boat, Hermes and a woman with a black himation).

Case 87

Lekythoi from the mature period of the Achilles painter. The outlines are matt, the meeting with death shrouds the figures in mys-

No. 1818 White lekythos by the Achilles painter

No. 1935 Large official white lekythos by the Bosanquet painter

No. 17916 White lekythos with polychrome design. Charon in his boat, Hermes and a woman

144

tery. No. **12480**. Red-figure lekythos by the same painter. Two women (Muses?). No. **1760**. With a servant girl carrying water, is by the Quadrate painter. So is no. **1957**, with its unusual double motif (tomb and stele), and also no. **1925** (laying out of a dead woman).

Case 91

No. **1183**. Official pelike. A *kithara*-player, Nike carrying water, and another symbolic figure flying (without wings). By the Athens 1183 painter, one of the last "mannerists". *Circa* 450 B.C. No. **16260** is by the same man. Two *Nikai* are leading an ox to the sacrifice. Tripod, Satyr (victory in a dithyrambic competition). The same man also produced the three pelikai with common subjects, nos. **1186**, **18731**, **18732**. No. **1291**. Low pyxis. On the lid Perseus and the Graiai (Old Women; all three of whom have one eye and one tooth between them). The Phiale painter, a perceptive pupil of the Achilles painter, produced the pyxides nos. **1587**, **1588**, the white lekythos no. **1940**, and the red-figure lekythos no. **1598**. *Circa* 430 B.C.

Case 92

White, black-figure lekythoi with matt outlines. Nos. **19353-19362**. These ten white lekythoi were discovered in a stone sarcophagus at Anavyssos. No. **19357** is one of the best works by the Bird painter.

On a separate stand

No. **18063**. Brilliant large stamnos, from a bequest by Damianos Kyriazis. The painting is one of the most superb products of the vase-painter Polygnotos. The body is rose coloured, and the lid is volute-haped. Rape of a young woman by a youth carrying a spear. On the right is a man in a chariot, and at the side a woman. The figures are named; Theseus, Helen, Peirithous, Phoibe. It is a representation of the legend of the rape of Helen in Sparta by Theseus and his friend. *Circa* 420 B.C.

Case 95

No. **1489**. Small lebes (dinos). The hunting of the Kaledonian boar. Work by one of the "mannerists", the Agrigento painter. The pelike no. **12492** is by the same man. Battle of the Amazons. So is no. **1399**. A. Satyr on a table and Maenad. No. **12463**. Red-figure kylix. Nos. **17921**, **1417**. Pelike. Dionysos and Maenad. Nos. **5883** and **5894**. Two small figurines. Delightful picture of a woman with a hydria; a figure with a lion's head water-spout. No. **2181**. Epinetron; head of a goddess at the front of it. On the sides are red-figure paintings of young men and women.

Case 96

No. **1260**. Hydria. Sappho (named), seated and holding an inscribed tablet. Three of her friends. By a painter from the circle of Polygnotos. No. **14983**. Large hydria. Menelaos rushing at Helen. From the hand of the vase-painter Polygnotos. No. **12883**. Hydria; music in the women's rooms. Charming painting by the Peleus painter. The Kassel painter produced the two fine pelikai nos. **1467**

No. 18063 Red-figure stamnos, by the painter Polygnotos

(Apollo and the two Muses) and **1469** (*kithara*-player, judge, Nike), and also the hydria no. **1177** (two women and a man). No. **1700**. Part of a loutrophoros. Three stelai and warriors (the "public grave"); by the Kleophon painter. No. **2179**. Epinetron. On the end of it is Pegasus, and on one side, a seated woman with an epinetron on her knee. Nos. **2180** and **2182**. Two later epinetra. On the end is a head of a goddess. No. **1167**. Krater of Corinthian type. Prometheus the fire bearer. Satyr dance. By the Orpheus painter. So is the pelike no. **1418**, with its lively picture of a man with a purse suspiciously eyeing a youth. No. **1166**. Amphora with broad mouth. Triptolemos in his chariot. No. **14793**. Clay semicircular impression: Europa, naked, holding lightly to the horns of Zeus, the bull. Dolphins. "From the southern coast of Crete".

On a separate stand

No. **17918**. Brilliant hydria. Music in the women's room. One woman, standing (the bride?) is holding a pyxis. One of the best works by the Peleus painter.

Case 94

Nos. **19333-19350**. White lekythoi discovered in a simple stone sarcophagus at Anavyssos in Attica. No. **19333**. Woman and youth, beautiful figures. No. **19342**. Charon in his boat, with a woman in front. No. **19335**. Charming little girl with a hydria on her head. No. **19338**. A mourning woman kneeling under a tree. No. **19337**. A beautiful stele, the anthemia on double volutes. All by the Bird painter, "an unusually delicate work from his final period". (Beazley, on the lekythoi nos. **19333-19338**).

Case 97

No. **1185**. Pelike, from the hand of Aison. Farewells to a youth; inscriptions: Theseus, Aithra. No. **17983**. Low pyxis with star gods, the Sun etc. No. **1962**. White lekythos. Youth with lyre, and other figures. No. **1833**. Large lekythos. The better lekythos, no. **2028**, with the young woman opposite Charon, is from the productive hand of the Reed painter. Blue colour for the river Acheron. Red for the outlines. By the same man: nos. **1759** (Charon) and **1766**. No. **17469**. Red-figure hydria with seven women. Because of the symbolism of the subject, they have been interpreted as the seven Pleiades. *Circa* 410 B.C.

Case (without number) on the south wall

Nos. **1172** and **1250**. Two nuptial lebetes and a loutrophoros. On the belly is a wedding. There are four divinities on the base. No. **1249**. Loutrophoros. Wedding. The groom is leading the bride with his hand on her wrist. By the Boreas painter. *Circa* 420 B.C.

No. **14792**. Large plate. The figures are standing on a horizontal line, with anthemia below. Helen, the sponsor, Paris and a young woman. Work with the Classical calm of the Washing painter; the obsolete form of the plate is rare.

Nuptial lebetes. No. **1171**. The women's quarters. A woman playing the lyre, Erotes etc. By the Athens 1454 painter, named after the similar lebes no. **1454**, with the seated bride being crowned by a woman (Aphrodite?). There are paintings of excellent quality on the two nuptial lebetes nos. **14790** and **14791**, with scenes of the women's quarters. No. **14791**. A seated woman and a woman playing the harp.

No. 17918 Brilliant hydria by the Peleus painter

No. 1218 Chous vase used in the Anthesteria

Work of the Washing painter. Only the lid has survived of the lebes no. **1681**. The painting is akin to that of the Meidias painter.

Nos. **1488** and **14500**. Two lebetes (dinoi) by the Dinos painter showing Dionysos and his entourage (*thiasos*). The refined, airy design on the first is characteristic of the painter. No. **1453**. Loutrophoros with wedding procession, by the Loutrophoros painter. *Circa* 430 B.C.

This case contains numerous choes, the vases of the Anthesteria were held by small children on the second day of this popular festival; some of them have funerary motifs. The two choes nos. **1218-1219** are amongst the largest, showing the drunken god Dionysos, who celebrated along with the Athenians. No. **1221**. Woman surprised by a Satyr standing on a rock. The most charming are the small choes, with children wearing the "crown of leaves". Found in the graves of young children. Nos. **1226**, **1229**. Two of the most splendid children's choes.

Case 99

Large white lekythoi. The two famous ones, nos. **1816** and **1817** are the best works of the main painter of the "R group". The dead man, inconsolable, is sitting on the ledge of the stele (development in depth). Matt red outlines. *Circa* 410 B.C. The majority of the lekythoi in this case are works of the Triglyph painter, one of the last of the lekythos painters (390-380 B.C.). The drawing is easy and forceful, and the outlines here are red: cf. nos. **1755**, **1770**, **1831**, **1840**. No. **1908** with a woman sitting in front of a stele. No. **1796** has the obsolete subject of the laying out of the dead. In no. **1755** there is a powerful picture of a dead woman with her hair untied. The large lekythos no. **1830**, with the milky coat, has been restored from numerous fragments, because it was purposely smashed on the deceased's grave by his loved ones. The superb representation, now no longer visible, is known from an earlier drawing: Sleep and Death place a young woman in her grave, in front of a stele. Hermes behind. At the edge, traces of Charos in his boat.

ROOM 56 (of the «epinetron from Eretria»)

Case 103

A number of works by the Eretria painter, who derives his name from no. **1629**, the famous "epinetron from Eretria". Fine plastic bust of Aphrodite on the small side. Around the edges are painted Peleus and Thetis and on the sides, the bride Alkestis lying on her bed, and friends of hers. B. Harmonia, Eros, Himeros, Aphrodite. These scenes from the women's quarters are covered by the divine robe of myth. *Circa* 430 B.C. The enchanting scene of a symposium on the chous no. **15308**, with a young woman on a bed and a young woman playing the harp, is by the same painter, as are the cups

No. 1816 World-famous, large white lekythos. The deceased in front of his grave

No. 1629 The much-praised epinetron, from Eretria

Nos. 2059-2060 Two plastic vases from a grave at Tanagra

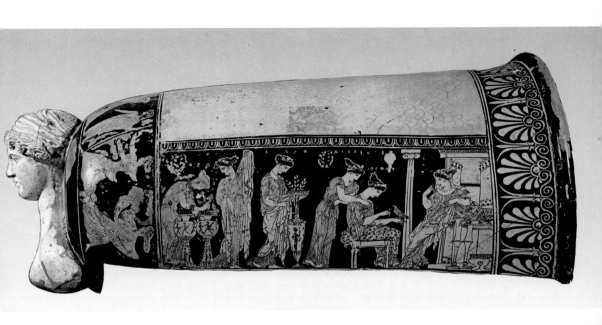

No. 1226 Small chous, vase used in the Anthesteria

No. 1333 The Gigantomachy pelike. From Tanagra

nos. **17539**, **1570**. The small loutrophoros no. **12540** reflects works by the Eretria painter; the bride is holding a loutrophoros. The vases by the Meidias painter, with their exaggerated femininity in the female figures, reflect a later phase of Attic vase-painting, at the time of Alkibiades, 420-410 B.C. No. **1179**. Hydria; the festival of Adonis. No. **1695**. Red-figure lekythos. A woman is sacrificing a pig to Hekate Genetyllis, with torches set up in the earth. The women's festival of Adonis was the subject of another vase – the fragment no. **19522**, discovered at Argos. Beautiful girl, with a ladder behind her. The low pyxides nos. **1369**, **1243**, **1630** are painted with the later technique, which involved the application of a white colour (to the detriment of the line). No. **1630** is the best. Its lid and body are both decorated. Wedding. Beginning of the fourth century B.C. The small, delicate kylikes, nos. **1571**, **1572**, **14514**, are the work of the Fauvel painter. The walls are fine, the drawing somewhat lifeless. Bidding youths farewell. *Circa* 410 B.C.

The little vases, nos. **17542-17533** are from a grave at Peristeri (Athens). On the small aryballos a charming school scene.

Case 104

No. **1284**. Lekythos without shoulder, acorn-shaped at the bottom. Romantic scene in a verdant spot. Traces of gold on the wings of Eros. Very delicate drawing. No. **19279**. Circular clay impression. B. Nereid on the body of a Triton. Model for the cover of a bronze mirror or for the lid of a metal pyxis. No. **19367**. Clay figurine of a serene goddess, sitting on a throne. No. **1573**. Cup without a base. Bride and Erotes. No. **13605**. Clay figurine of a young woman performing a daring acrobatic leap. No. **1246**. Small skyphos of the Corinthian type (kotyle). Two ethereal figures. A. Maenad with drum. B. Similar one: Chimaerophonos. *Circa* 410 B.C. "The drawing is very close to the Shuvalov Painters" (Beazley). No. **17753**. Miniature chous. Child with a dog, and a bird flying; the feeling of Spring. No. **1631**. Small oinochoe with a broad rim, and with very delicate drawing. Two horsemen, throwing the javelin at a shield.

On a separate stand

No. **1333**. The Gigantomachy pelike. Found at Tanagra. A. Ares at the top centre, with the Dioskouroi on either side of him. Below, four Giants, all depicted from behind. The composition is divided into three pairs of rivals. B. Four god-like youths in a verdant area (the Elysian fields?). The significance of the Gigantomachy is probably also eschatological. Close to the Pronomos painter. *Circa* 400 B.C.

Case 108

The Eleusinian three-handled skyphos no. **1341** is from the same tomb as the pelike no. **1333**. Between the handles are Demeter, Kore and Eumolpos. By the Diomedes painter. Nos. **17192-17197**. Alabastron and a fine three-footed pyxis. No. **17191**. Pyxis with stopper. No. **13676**. Small pyxis with pieces of cosmetics. On the lid there are three female heads (Aphrodite?). No. **1442**. Larger pyxis; women and Erotes. No. **1388**. Calyx krater. The scene is in two bands. Marriage procession. The man on the upper left is throwing a shoe. By the Athens wedding painter. No. **1693**. Bell-krater. Large censer in the middle, and youths. By the Kadmos painter. No. **13027**. Dinos. Flute-player wearing a sleeved chiton, and dancers in a Satyr play. This picture makes an important contribution to the history of the ancient theatre. By the Athenian Dinos painter. *Circa* 410 B.C.

Case 106

No. **2060**. Plastic vase (aryballos-shaped lekythos). Bust of Aphrodite Anadyomene. She is framed by two large shells. The exposed parts of her body are white, and the rest of the decoration is gold. It is from the same tomb at Tanagra as the Gigantomachy pelike (on the stand), as is also the next plastic vase, no. **2059**, a lekythos on a square base. A winged spirit with a thick cloak and a chlamys (Death?) is supporting a young woman, who is falling, by the arms. Both these fine figures are white.

ROOM 56 (Vases from the fourth century)

Case 107 (Vases from the G. Empedokleos donation)

No. **18709**. Red-figure cup. A youth and a krater, on the interior emblem. By the Euergides painter. No. **18828**. Aryballos-shaped lekythos. A woman in her room. No. **18844**. Pelike. Flute-player and dancer. No. **19390**. Fragment of an oinochoe. Satyr and a Maenad worshipping Dionysos "Dendrites". Of the Maenad, only the hand crowning the tree is preserved. No. **18015**. Part of an oinochoe (chous). The dead Chimaera, with Athena on the left and the body of a young man (Bellerephon) on the right. No. **18572**. Small red-figure lekythos. Woman. Six small early lekythoi with a yellowish slip, and others with a white slip. A number of good black-figure vases. No. **18722**. Cup. A man rolling a great stone or rock. Sisyphos? The hasty drawing is reminiscent of vases by the Pithos painter.

On the long table opposite

Panathenaic amphoras from Eretria, amongst the best from the fourth century. They are black-figure, however, as a result of a traditional devotion by the city of Athens to the earlier technique. On the one side is Athena Promachos in a conventional archaising stance, and on the other, athletes taking part in the *pankration*, wrestling and boxing. The drawing is free, and the contents intensely rendered. It is dated by the names of the Archontes: "Charikleides was archon" (363/2 B.C.) and "Archon Kallimedes" (360/59 B.C.).

Case 120

Vases from the Boeotian shrine of the Kabeiroi. Although most of them are from the Classical period, the vase-painters have predominantly used the black-figure style. The parodies of myths are particularly entertaining. No. **10426**. Skyphos. The man lying down is named (Kabeiros), as are the other figures. Two are fierce looking. No. **10470**. The upper part of an amphora. On the neck is the inscription: "Smikros dedicated [me] to Kabeiros". Nos. **10486** and **10487**. Plastic vases in the form of Silenus. No. **10459**. Clay bobbin. In the centre: A. Perseus, with a white slip around him. B. Medusa. No. **10453**. Black-painted rhyton with the

Panathenaic amphora. From Eretria

No. 12486 Large Boeotian kantharos

151

No. 15113 Attic amphora

head of an ass. Skyphoi with plant decoration and with parodies of gods and myths.

Case (without number)

No. **10466**. Large Kabeirian skyphos. A. Two pairs of Kabeiroi lying on a mattress. Flute-player and a naked ithyphallic youth dancing. B. Kabeiroi on a mattress. Most of these vases present lively pictures of the mysteries of the Kabeiroi. Three large Boeotian red-figure kantharoi. Nos. **1372** and **12487**. Feasting of a chthonian hero. No. **12486**. Bellerephon on Pegasus. Boeotian works, with Attic influence, but having a secret Boeotian eschatological meaning.

Case 109

Attic vases from the end of the fifth and the beginning of the fourth century B.C. The prevailing shape is the calyx krater and the painting is dominated by the applied white colour which initially is discreetly confined to the centre, but which later spreads to other parts. Dionysos, the main figure, is always depicted beardless. No. **12253**. Calyx krater. Ancient shrine. Tripod with acanthus column in the centre. Dionysos lying down, other figures. No. **14902**. A similar one. Herakles sitting in his tetrastyle building (without roof). No. **11559**. A similar one. A. Banquet. B. Three youths. By the Uppsala painter. No. **12603**. Calyx krater, with very delicate drawings. Dionysos, Eros and a group of revellers. Early. There is no white slip. The hand of the same painter can be seen in the two kraters nos. **1366** (sacrifice of an ox) and **1395** (young suppliant at an altar, with a sword, and two other figures). Painter of Athens 1366.

Case 119

Boeotian vases. No. **12593**. Small bell-shaped krater. Danae, raised up on her bed, receiving the golden rain. No. **17300**. Black-figure chous. Satyr, krater and a goat in a cave. Nos. **4044**, **4052** and **6006**. Clay figurines of women making bread. No. **1385**. Calyx krater. The triad of Apollo, the *kithara*-player, Leto and Artemis. Imitation of an Attic vase, as are many Boeotian vases. No. **5676**. Clay figurines. Youth holding a cock, the nude parts of the body red. No. **1406**. Large skyphos. A Nymph or goddess bathing. Above, Satyrs look on, not without some threat of danger.

On a separate stand

The brilliant Attic amphora no. **15113**. In the centre: Atalanta and Meleagros, three youths and three figures with "embroidered" chitons. By the Meleagros painter.

Case 110

Charming little Attic hydrias (nos. **12546**, **17297**, **12424**, **19500**) with rich anthemia on the back. There is applied white colour on the central figures. No. **12546** (no white colour) Poseidon and Amymone. No. **17297**. Eleusinian deities. Demeter sitting on a stone, Kore, Herakles and Iachos. No. **1424**. Maenads, Dionysos and Eros. No. **19500**. Eros playing castanets in the centre. Maenad on the left and a young Satyr "taking aim" on the right. No. **12595**. The

Paposeilinos calyx krater. White buskins on the bottom. No. **4692**. Figurine of a woman from Tanagra. She is wearing a *pilos* and holding a fan. Charming. *Circa* 330 B.C. Small choes; no. **1164** is bigger. No. **17752**. A unique subject. A small boy sitting on a low stool is holding a chous; on the left is an ithyphallic figure wearing a mask, and on the right is a small boy running and holding an artificial snake. It is perhaps a picture of the purification of Orestes, which was one of the mythical reasons for the festival of the Choes. *Circa* 380 B.C.

On a separate stand

Large red-figure krater with one handle. A large egg on an altar with the child Helen appearing from the crack in it. Above is the eagle-Zeus. On the left, Leda, startled and at the edges, the Dioskouroi. Local work, possibly by a Lakonian painter, with a rare lucidity in the portrayal of the miracle.

Case 118

Some of the vases in this case are from the same site at Vourvoura, Arkadia. The fragment with Thetis on a sea horse, bringing Achilles' weapons, is probably from a Corinthian vase. On the fragment no. **19453**, from an Attic hydria, the seated Athena is well drawn. Some of the vases are of local manufacture. No. **19450**. Large black-painted krater-oinochoe with an ivy shoot. No. **19454**. Black-glaze krater with volute handles ("Lakonian" type). No. **19448**. Red-figure oinochoe. Owl. Local work like the calyx krater no. **19452**.

Case 111

Attic vases. Calyx kraters. The shape still has the seriousness of the fifth century B.C. The use of the applied white is discreet. No. **12490**. Dionysos and Ariadne, band of revellers and Erotes. By the Erbach painter. No. **12605**. Nike in a chariot ("Telos group"). No. **1363**. Similar krater. Dionysos walking arm in arm with Ariadne and a band of revellers. No. **2336**. Slender black-glaze hydria with relief flutings. No. **12674**. Calyx krater. Two youths and a man wearing a *pilos*. No. **1244**. Fragment of a plaque.

Case 117

Mainly Corinthian works. No. **12260**. Hydria. Women's quarters. No. **537**. Small plate; kore seated on an official throne, holding a torch, ears of corn and poppy shoots. The whole picture is framed in black. Nos. **4400-4404**. Five jointed, clay figurines (νευρόσπαστα) from a tomb. No. **4412**. A goddess seated on a simple throne. Nos. **5963**, **4140** and **4141**. Small figurines of young women, seated. The first is holding an open papyrus. No. **1412**. Large skyphos. Horseman and youthful trumpeters. No. **4160**. Very fine figurine of the Corinthian Aphrodite, with the young Eros near her. *Circa* 360 B.C. No. **1712**. Small plate. Pegasus. No. **1382**. Attic bell-shaped krater with two frenzied dancers, presaging a dance of Maenads. The transcendental mystery shrouding the Attic krater, no. **1435**, led to the interpretation of the figures as "pure heroes", dead who escaped from the Isles of the Blessed. *Circa* 370 B.C.

No. 12490 Kalyx krater with Dionysos and his thiasos

No. 4160 Figurine, Aphrodite with the young Eros. From Corinth

153

Case 112

Attic vases from the fourth century B.C. No. **1443**. Hydria. Dionysos and Eleusinian deities. No. **1472**. Pelike. Delightful picture of three women bathing. *Circa* 330 B.C. By the Athens painter. No. **15851**. Nuptial lebes without a base. The bride is seated, holding a fine basket, in the centre. There is abundant use of white. Nos. **11704** and **18746**. Small pelikai with covers. Dionysos seated, Eros and a Maenad. On both covers is painted the head of a goddess (Aphrodite). From the L-C group (Late Calyx Kraters). There is an important picture on the delicate skyphos-kotyle no. **13909**. Herakles and Athena, the latter a free rendering of the type of Athena leaning on her shield. Small choes (nos. **1224**, **1232**, **14542**, **13031**). White paint on the bare flesh of the children in the later ones.

On separate stands

No. **2578**. Nuptial lebes. Graceless drawing. In the centre of the room. No. **14899**. Large calyx krater: A. A tree, Greeks and Orientals. B. An Asian fighting a griffin. The narrow shape with high handles was the predominant one until the last quarter of the fourth century B.C.

Table 116

Three calyx kraters. No. **1328**. A. Epiphany of Aphrodite on the Swan. B. Dionysos and Erotes and a seated Maenad. No. **12592**. A similar one. A. Sanctuary of Dionysos, very delicate drawing. Dionysos seated, Maenads, Satyrs. A Bull on a high, white Ionic column. B. Aphrodite on the Swan. By the Athens 12592 painter. No. **14901**. A similar one. A. Dionysos, Maenad playing the harp. B. Four-wheel chariot.

Table 115

Three calyx kraters. No. **12545**. A. The judgement of Paris (wearing trousers). B. Satyrs and Maenad. The L-C group. No. **12544**. Aphrodite weighing two small Erotes (on a scale), Hermes. By the "Erotostasia" painter. The body of Aphodite is white. *Circa* 330 B.C.

Case 113

No. **1718**. Rich pelike, with a range of colours – white, blue, gold. The bride, sitting on a chair, is accepting a very skilfully worked basket from a friend. Below her is a small Eros, and others are flying on high. On the left is a young woman with a mirror, and on the right two women in a relaxed stance. The linear rendition of these three figures is very delicate. B. Dionysos seated, a small Eros behind him, a Maenad with a drum, walking on tiptoe, and a Satyr. It has a broad mouth, like the pelikai from the middle of the fourth century. No. **11037**. Skyphos from Eleusis. A. Triptolemos. B. Dionysos (?) and a goddess. (The centre is missing). According to the inscription it was dedicated to Demeter by Demetria. Work of the Marsyas painter, who produced some of the best fourth-century vases. No. **4696**. Clay Tanagra figurine, one of the most dreamlike. She is wearing a *pilos* and holding a fan. No. **1204**. Large aryballos-shaped lekythos. The women's quarters. Nos. **1325-6**. Two pyxides

No. 4696 Superb terracotta Tanagra figurine

with covers. No. **1635**. Three-footed pyxis. Leto, supporting herself on the palm-tree, in the pangs of giving birth to Apollo on Delos. Behind her are two Eileithyia, the goddesses of childbirth, and in front Athena, leaning on a shield (imitating a statue of the goddess). White paint, gold for the decoration. No. **1370**. Krater by the Athens painter.

Case 114

No. **1181**. Pelike. A. The judgement of Paris, who is sitting deep in thought and wearing trousers. Hermes and the three goddesses. Eris is sticking her head forward at the top left. One of the best works by the Marsyas painter. Nos. **12527** and **12528**. Two lekanides with covers. The women's quarters with Erotes. Abundant use of white. No. **1370** is by the Athens painter. No. **1376**. Calyx krater with a Dionysian scene. No. **1378**. A similar one. Dionysos and Thiasos and a dancing girl. No. **1457**. A similar one. A white ithyphallic Herm. Altar tree. Men and women. No. **19463**. A similar one. Pan attacking a Maenad who is making a frightened gesture. No. **12543**. A similar one. An Eros on tiptoe on an altar and Maenads.

No. **42894**. Foot of a nuptial lebes. Dreamy dancers in short chitons, one is playing the lyre. On low stands, three small kraters.

No. 12544 Kalyx krater

On the wall

No. **11036**. The plaque of Ninnion. Dedication in the Sanctuary at Eleusis. It is in the shape of a small temple with a pediment and a central akroterion. The main subject, which is inspired by some preliminary stage of the initiations into the Eleusinian mysteries, is composed in two bands. The ancient Eleusinian goddess is seated above, with Kore standing in front of her holding a torch and receiving a young woman; the latter is wearing a vase, the kernos, instead of the hat (*pilos*). There are a boy and a man behind her. Below ,on the right, is Demeter, seated, with the mystic chest behind her and a kind of navel in front of her. On the left is Iachos holding a torch, a young woman and a man. Below, on the cornice is the inscription "Ninnion [dedicated me] to the gods". Ninnion may be recognised in the figure at the top with the kernos on her head. The four figures on the pediment have been interpreted as reflecting the "all night festival". 370-350 B.C.

No. 11036 Plaque of Ninnion. From Eleusis

PLAN OF THE 1ST FLOOR OF THE NATIONAL ARCHAEOLOGICAL MUSEUM

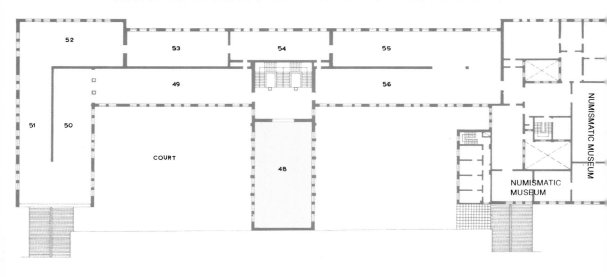

Thera exhibition

The Numismatic Museum (Upper Floor)

The Numismatic Museum is temporarily housed in three galleries in the south wing of the first floor. It includes ancient Greek coins from the Greek colonies, the Greek Mainland and islands, Asia Minor, Bactria, India, Cyrenaica and Mauritania, as well as Roman and Byzantine coins and jewellery. In the near future the Numismatic Museum will be housed in the *Iliou Melathron.*

Thera Exhibition (Upper Floor)

ROOM 48

This room houses finds from the excavations on Thera, including representative products of pottery, bronze-work and stone-work, and the remains of precious frescoes, which are brilliant examples of painting, and afford much information about life on Thera at the end of the sixteenth century B.C. The volcanic tephra, which covered the surface of the earth with a thick stratum after the terrible eruption, has helped to preserve large fragments of wall-paintings in very good condition, and these have now been restored in a most impressive fashion.

On separate stands

Prochoi (jugs) (nos. **1111**, **1172**), amphoras (nos. **1171**, **1167**, **1264**, **1168**) and stamnoi (nos. **1154**, **437**).

Case 1

Representative examples of local and imported pottery. The vases are mainly of the matt-painted type. There are jugs, one of which is decorated with barley ears (no. **928**), and another of which is a nippled jug. The vase no. **562** has a pierced bottom. It is not known

No. 922 Kyathos

No. 928 Jug

No. 100 Kymbe with dolphins

No. 563 Clay rhyton

what it was used for. The kyathoi (nos. **922, 932**) are also typical, while the beaked jug (no. **89**) with the reddish-brown red decoration, is an import.

Case 2

Local matt-painted vases. Representative examples are the nippled jugs (nos. **1107, 1179**), and no. **877**, which is imitating a long-beaked bird. There are also five bowls with lilies (no. **564**), dolphins (no. **100**), swallows (no. **101**) and animals running amongst plants (nos. **3266, 3267**). The two twin vases (nos. **1279, 1280**) are curious; they have been interpreted as flower vases.

Case 3

This contains mainly imported Creto-Mycenaean vases: cups with central ribs, askoi, stirrup jars, amphoras, and a vessel for pouring (no. **230**). Two Minoan jugs are outstanding; one (no. **1253**) has thick reed decoration, while the other (no. **74**) has plants hanging down.

Case 4

Vases in the local technique. There are rhytons, cups and two small clay oxen from a sacrificial fire (nos. **597, 598**). The clay rhyton (no. **563**) has the shape of an ox and was covered with a net-pattern. Amongst the collection of sherds in representative style the sinewy face of a "man of the forests" (no. **1387**) is outstanding. Other notable items include the pouring vessel (no. **1470**) with the reed decoration, and the strainer (no. **99**).

On separate stands

There are two large unpainted jugs that are not in cases. One (no. **1372**) has a Linear A inscription on its shoulder, and the other is incised with the "stool" symbol. The strainer (no. **565**) has a pierced bottom and is decorated with continuous spirals.

Case 5

Unusual vessels and the remains of organic substances. The two clay supports with notches (nos. **1463, 1464**) were the uprights of a grill, on which a large number of small spits could be placed. There is also a table (no. **1376**) with a hollow in which coals were placed to keep food hot, and two braziers (nos. **1441, 989**) with clear traces of coals.

Case 6

Bronze objects (jugs, trays). One of the jugs has a schematic papyrus flower on its shoulder, in a "magic combination" in which the flower of one plant serves as the calyx of the next. There is also a clay rhyton (no. **1855**) in the shape of a lion's head, indicating an original in metal.

There are two jugs outside the case (nos. **994, 1176**).

Case 7

Representative objects in this case are the tall cylindrical vessels (nos. **1007, 1030, 154, 155**), which have been interpreted as flower vases, the sickles (nos. **125, 126, 127**), and a rectangular slate plaque (no. **134**) on which the young pupils scratched drawings and learned their first letters. There is also a series of disc-shaped pieces of unknown use and a clay rhyton in the shape of a lion's head (no. **116**).

Outside the case: the grapes jug (no. **623**), two jugs with paintings of dolphins (nos. **1515, 1516**), offering tables of painted plaster and the cast of a wooden bed – the earliest in the area of Aegean civilisation. A modern construction of the same type, made of olive wood, stands next to it to help the visitor to reconstruct the complete form of the bed.

Wall-paintings

The wall-painting with the large decorative *lilies* came from the "House of the Ladies", as did the *"Wall-painting of the Ladies",* which is substantially destroyed. The women's faces have fine features. The women are wearing the coloured Minoan skirt and short jacket; there is a symbolic depiction of the starry sky above their heads.

The wall-painting of the "naval expedition". This is a miniature wall-painting in which the artist gives a narrative of a naval expedition in a continuous frieze with a large number of figures; it may possibly refer to some specific event. Six metres of the complete frieze have been preserved, depicting the 7 warships, a large number of smaller boats, three cities, about 8 human figures and a variety of domestic and wild animals. The facility with which the painting is executed, the skilful composition, the wealth of colour, and the inventiveness of the painter, all make it unique.

Another miniature wall-painting is exhibited along with it: animals, birds and a griffin move amongst tropical vegetation.

The wall-painting of the "fisherman". One of the best preserved wall-paintings. The fisherman is shown naked, holding two bunches of fish tied with yellow string. The naturalistic inclination of the artist is most intense here.

The wall-painting with the young "priestess" is yet another example of the artistic dexterity of the Minoan painters on Thera. The *"Banner"* exhibited next to it, in its present form of restoration, may perhaps depict the façade of a temple or shrine.

The wall-painting of Spring. This is without doubt the most wonderful painting of all. It presents a picture of a purely Theran landscape in the days before the eruption. The subject, the rebirth of nature in the Spring, is unfolded as a single, unified whole. Solid rocks in unexpected shapes and a wide range of colours, typical of volcanic rock, rise steeply upwards. On their crests and slopes, and in the ravines between them, grow clumps of lilies with golden-yellow stems and bright red flowers full of delicate charm and lively beauty – from the bud to the dying flower. Swallows, painted in perspective, fly amongst them and flirt with each other.

Wall-painting of the "monkeys". Remains of figures of blue monkeys climbing steep rocks pursued by dogs.

Wall-painting of the boxing children. Two boys are boxing, with enchanting seriousness. The fresco emits an air of sensitive tenderness and a charming disposition. One of the most attractive examples of Minoan painting on Thera.

Wall-painting of antelopes. The whole graceful flexibility of the animals has been rendered here with flowing lines and a unique simplicity of conception.

No. 116 Clay rhyton in the form of a lion's head

The wall-painting of the fisherman

The wall-painting from the House of the Ladies

The wall-painting of the "naval expedition"

Wall-painting with a subtropical landscape 163

The wall-painting of the boxing children

wall-painting of Spring

The wall-painting of Antilopes

GROUND PLAN OF THE MAIN FLOOR

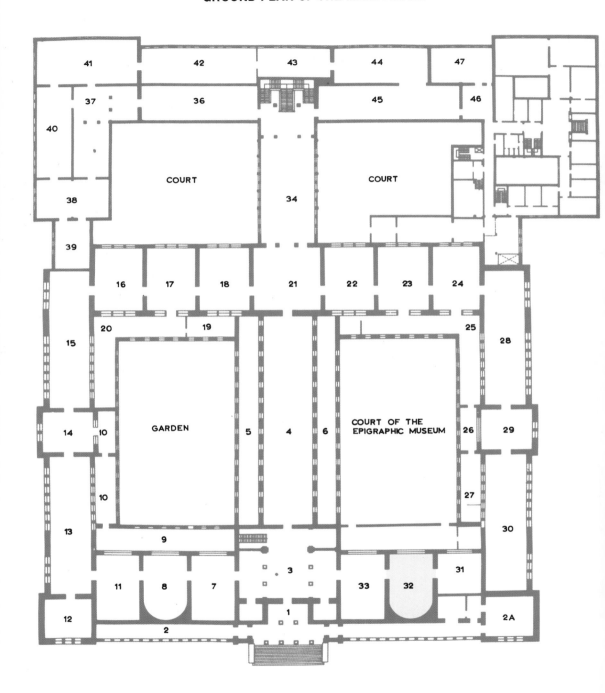

Stathatos collection

The Helen Stathatos
Collection (Ground Floor)

ROOM 32

The Helen Stathatos Collection will soon be exhibited in Room 40 on the ground floor.

This room contains ancient and Byzantine objects, all of which were presented by Helen Stathatos, who over the years assembled this collection with love and determination, and with great financial sacrifice, intending always to present it to her country.

On a separate stand

On the right as one enters the room from the interior of the Museum: a fine Geometric oinochoe (**St. 364**) of the second half of the eighth century B.C., with decoration.

Case 8

Vases, clay figurines and stone objects from various periods. **St. 70**, **421** and **422**. Small stone vases from the Early Minoan period, one of them a pyxis with lid. **St. 38**. Three-footed stone vase. **St. 8**. Mycenaean clay figurine. The epiphany of a goddess in a horse. **St. 11**. Chariot of Mycenaean period. **St. 43** and **44**. Marble Cycladic vases. **St. 18802**. Late Corinthian oinochoe from the beginning of the sixth century B.C. **St. 32**. Horseman. **St. 37**. Very fine Attic clay figurine depicting Athena seated on a throne. Beginning of the fifth century B.C. **St. 23** "Melian" clay relief. A Triton and a youth. **St. 27**. Clay figurine of a mourning woman. Boeotian work of about 550 B.C. **St. 1**. Clay alabastron with a fascinating painting of a young woman. By the Syriskos painter, about 460 B.C. **St. 2**. Small lekythos with a

No. 30 Clay figurine of Hermes

167

No. 493 Byzantine jewellery

No. 352 Gold earring

yellow slip. Persephone in Hades. Fine delicate work by the Providence painter. 460-450 B.C.

On a separate stand

St. 315. The neck of an outstanding large krater with volute handles. Black-figure scenes. A. Duel between Herakles and Kyknos. In the middle, Zeus, left, Athena. B. Herakles and the Nemean lion. The lustrous black glaze which covered the main body has not survived. The vase had been dedicated on the Acropolis.

On separate stands, below the windows

St. 30. Clay Boeotian statuette of Hermes carrying a ram. *Circa* 440 B.C.

St. 330. Marble portrait head of a woman, formerly set on a statue. The nose is slightly hooked, and the parting of the hair is wavy. Fine product of the third century A.D. Expressionism, probably from the hand of an Asia Minor sculptor. It probably comes from Constantinople. **St. 708**. Clay figurine of Aphrodite. Dressed in a "wet chiton", she is leaning with her right elbow on the upright wing of Eros and has her other arm round a tree. A combination of the "Frejus" Aphrodite type with the Aphrodite in the Gardens. Third century B.C. From Macedonia.

Cases 9-12

Below the windows to the right of the exit. Byzantine jewellery of various types and periods (case 11, **St. 620, 493, 740, 510** – case 12, **St. 745, 523, 489**). Silver cross (case 10, **St. 651**) with the inscription: "Lord, aid the wearer". Bronze lamps (case 12, **St. 430-432**), with their bases. Bronze eagle (case 12, **St. 539**), from Constantinople.

Left of the door, **St. 325-326**. Bronze helmet of Corinthian type. The mask, in a unique technique, comes from another tomb and is made of sheet gold.

Case 7

St. 726 and **129**. Silver pins. **St. 202-205**. Fibulae. **St. 186**. Two small gold vases with lovely rosette-shaped handle. **St. 187-188**. Other smaller ones. **St. 574**. Necklace with five small pendant amphoras. **St. 108-109**. Silver bracelets. **St. 125**. Silver pin with a fine rosette on the knob at the top. Peloponnesian work of the Classical period. **St. 597**. Gold earring with precious stones. Fifth century A.D.

On separate stands

St. 698. Small bronze temple, with winged Nemesis-Nike, *en face*, inside it. A wheel on the lower left. Third or beginning of the fourth century A.D.

St. 323-324. Two clay protomes of Alexander the Great. From Macedonia. Stereotyped passion of the end of the second century B.C.

No. 379 Gold object in the shape of a small temple with Dionysos, a Satyr and a panther

Case 5

St. 387. Small votive bronze shield depicting Kaineus sinking into the earth, with the rival Centaur next to him. Small bronze animals. **St. 382**. Female panther. **St. 331**. Steatite disc. Hermes in the centre, flanked by Harpokrates and Tyche. Asia Minor work of the third century A.D. (?).

On separate stands

Two bronze hammered covers of mirrors. **St. 312**. Herakles and Auge (?). **St. 313**. Achilles and Troilos (?). One of the most perfect Corinthian products from the fourth century B.C., with the design carefully arranged in the circle. **St. 424**. Small clay head from a statue, probably of Dionysos, and probably from a Peloponnesian workshop. Excellent work of the first half of the third century B.C.

Case 3

Bronze objects. **St. 406**. Juror's tablet, with the inscription: "Eugeiton of Halieis". **St. 396**. Bronze statuette of a bull, with a long body. From a provincial workshop of the middle of the seventh century B.C. Other small bronze animals.

On separate stands

St. 316. Bronze statuette of a deer, with its long neck outstretched. Exceptionally fine art; dedication to Artemis. Middle of the fifth century B.C. **St. 19405**. Boeotian vase with a base ("fruitstand"). Polychrome plant decoration on the interior. Beginning of the sixth century B.C. **St. 222**. Geometric amphora. Mourning women on the neck, and seven one-horse chariots with riders on the main band of the belly. Second half of the eighth century B.C.

Case 1

St. 221. Figures of warriors, Centaurs, dancers etc., set in squares. **St. 223-224**. Simple undecorated rings from the Geometric period. **St. 259**. Gold brooches. Nine silver vases (on the bottom shelf) phiale (**St. 197**), oinochoe (**St. 213**) and others, from a hoard in Asia Minor (Sinope?). First half of the fifth century B.C. It is not sure whether they come from workshops in Asia Minor, Syria or Phoenicia. **St. 306**. Gold necklace from the third century B.C. **St. 292-3**. Two funerary "Orphic" gold plates from Crete, with inscriptions from the third or second century B.C. ("The soul seeks to drink from a fountain" etc.).

On separate stands

St. 328. Bronze statuette of Hermes carrying a ram and wearing the *petasos*. This brilliant, completely cast work will probably have been made in a Sikyonian workshop about 530 B.C. **St. 327**. Bronze statuette of a naked youth with a cloak over his left shoulder. The left leg is relaxed. *Circa* 430 B.C., possibly the work of a notable bronze-smith from the northern Peloponnese, with Attic influence.

No. 259 Two gold fibulae

No. 369 Gold medallion, from a pyxis(?), with a bust of Artemis

No. 306 Gold necklace

Nos. 359, 346 Gold bracelets

The remains of a bronze object on the head are unexplained, but suggest that this charming statuette was perhaps part of a larger composition.

Cases 2, 4, 6

The three hexagonal cases 2, 4, 6, in the centre contain the richest gold objects in the collection, which come from Hellenistic tombs in Thessaly. Case 2, **St. 359**. Gold bracelet with a double spiral ending in the head of a snake. **St. 346**. A similar one, with precious stones set in the gaps in the curling body. Diadems, one of them (case 6, **St. 339**) with a climbing plant *à jour* and an Eros in the centre. Case 6, **St. 340-344**. Necklaces. Case 6, **St. 342-343**. Bands with repoussé figures. Case 4, **St. 379**. The most dazzling object of all. A small gold temple with its architectural members covered with decoration. Relief figures of Dionysos, a Satyr and a panther are emerging from the interior. A unique work from the second half of the third or the beginning of the second century B.C., from an unknown workshop. Case 4, **St. 370-371**. Two valuable cylindrical bracelets, with heads of animals facing each other. Case 4, **St. 369**. Gold disc with an emblem. In the middle is a fine raised bust of Artemis with a quiver, surrounded by interlinked chains. The type of the goddess derives from a monumental work of the second half of the fourth century B.C. Case 4, **St. 372**. A rich gold belt with a "Heraklean knot" in the centre; the two plates connected with this central piece have excellent light circles with rosettes linking them. Probably from the third century B.C., from Thessaly. Case 2, **St. 356** and **357**. Two similar discs with chains and busts – the one of Artemis, the other of Aphrodite. The busts are excellently arranged in the circle. Case 2, **St. 353**. Long slender necklace of gold with glass inlays and a Heraklean knot in the centre. Case 2, **St. 347**. Gold pin crowned with a column capital bearing a statuette of Aphrodite and Eros. Fine art from the beginning of the first century B.C. Case 6, **St. 332**. Clay egg, with a unique dreamlike painting depicting life in the women's quarters. Close to the Eretria painter. The delicacy of the painting matches the fine clay object well. 430-420 B.C. Case 2, **St. 358**. Gold necklace consisting of two bands with pendants in the shape of amphoras. Case 2, **St. 351-352**. Earrings. Case 2, **St. 359**. Bracelets. Case 2, **St. 362**. Gold belt, made of two plates with many rosettes of various sizes and precious stones in the centre.

On a separate stand, to the left of the exit

St. 701. Two pieces of a bronze plaque, with men wearing the toga facing each other. A group of two people on the left, and one of four on the right; only the heads have been portrayed of the two figures in the background on a secondary plane. The original purpose of the whole plaque is unknown. It is a fine work from the early Imperial period (first century B.C.).

No. 370 Gold bracelet

No. 339 Gold diadem from the Hellenistic period

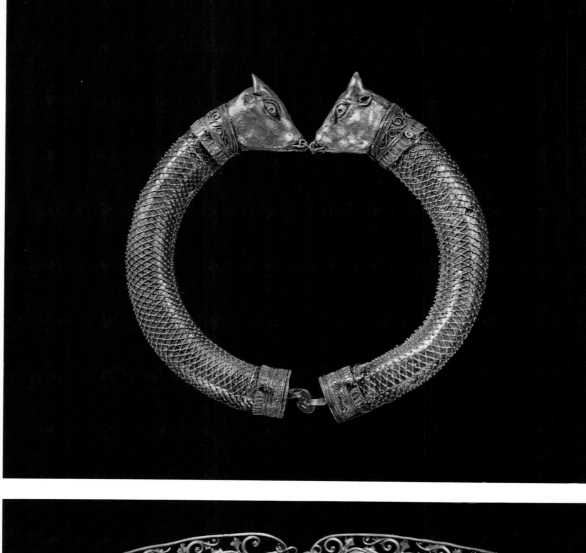